ONCE UPON A DIFFERENT TIME

MARIE ANNE MAYESKI

Upswing Publishing — San Diego, California

As clearly and cleverly explained on the cover, this is a fictionalized memoir. Almost everything described actually happened one way or another, mostly to the narrator. All the names have been changed, though, and many of the people described are no longer with us.

For permission requests, email the publisher with the subject "Attention: Permissions Coordinator"at
orders@upswingpublishing.com

Upswing Publishing
San Diego, CA
www.upswingpublishing.com

Special discounts are available on quantity purchases by corporations, associations and others. For details, send an email with the subject "Special Sales Department" to the address above.

ISBN (ebook) 978-1-942628-07-1
ISBN (paperback) 978-1-942628-06-4

Once Upon a Different Time

A memoir
with creative embellishments,
selective omissions,
imaginative digressions,
and only a few explicit untruths,
done for the purposes of entertainment.

But all the funny, poignant, and adventuresome bits
really happened,
and most of them happened
to me.

Acknowledgments

My thanks to the members of the Writer's Seminar, led by Joe Kronsberg at Emeritus College of Santa Monica City College. Their honest criticism, embedded in much encouragement and support, nudged this writing project forward.

My friend, Sharon Locy, is a member of this seminar. In addition to the critiques she offered in seminar meetings, Sharon generously read and re-read my work and gave suggestions that not only improved the text, but helped shape my process and thinking. No thanks would be extravagant enough to match her help.

Mary Lou Ward and Jean Jenkins were valued editors and my granddaughter, Susan Grace Veiga, kindly read the manuscript and gave a helpful evaluation of its potential audience.

My husband, Bill Evans, was an invaluable copyeditor. Beyond that, he believes in me and I depend on his quiet presence.

Dedication

To my five grandchildren, who are growing up well in yet a different time.

Prologue

Looking Back

I'VE GONE BACK ONLY ONCE and it was on a whim. My husband Joel had a series of business meetings on behalf of his IT company, something about a new product and the support services that came with it, a package he was attempting to sell. He usually made such trips alone, several times a year, but this time, I had reached the end both of the University semester and my latest publication project so I was free to join him for a little R & R. I planned to visit the Main New York Library on Fifth Avenue, hoping that a little random searching through the Berg collection of American lit might plant the seed of my next research idea. It must have been the library itself, the very smell of the place, that triggered the memories and the desire to see Haven Avenue again. I had a long afternoon before meeting Joel for a drink at the Oak Room of the Plaza so I took the Broadway subway to 181st Street.

The Haven Avenue I knew no longer exists. The street still runs near the Hudson River south of the George Washington Bridge. But my Haven Ave had been a single, long block north of the Bridge, cut off at one end by the bridge approach and, at the other, by 181st Street, leading to Riverside Drive. It seemed a world enclosed and we felt safe. A row of five-story apartment buildings lined each side of the street, but on our side, the river side, there was a large piece of seemingly abandoned property on the corner farthest from the bridge. A large house stood in the middle of the property where it gently deteriorated while it fed our imaginations.

We called that derelict house 'the mansion' and many were the stories we wove about it. Over the years we peopled it with different families, imagined the elaborate weddings we thought must have taken place there, decided that George Washington surely celebrated dinner there with his officers. The grounds were surrounded by a huge iron fence, and immovable gates protected the curving driveway that swept in and up to the front entrance. The fence turned the mansion into forbidden territory, but enterprising explorers who preceded us had pried up enough of the bars in one corner to allow us to go in and out at will. There were parks aplenty in Manhattan, but the mansion's grounds were the preferred place for dreaming, staging mock battles and real confrontations and holding private conferences with cohorts

The old mansion and its grounds, prime real estate as I later understood, succumbed eventually to the post-war thirst for housing and several large apartment houses took over the space. Then, by approving the construction of a lower level to the bridge, the Army Corps of Engineers accomplished what years of my father's persuasive arguments could not. The bridge construction would demolish their apartment house and my parents were forced to move. By then, two of Mother's sisters had already moved to California and my parents followed in 1959. So by the time I went back, the block looked entirely different.

I stand on the corner and close my eyes, bringing the mansion back in memory. Just there, at the corner where the bars had been pried up, I can see June climbing under and heading toward the back fence where she plans to meet Dennis O'Connor. Over on the old porch, Marilyn sits, sketching one of her designs and waiting for me to join her. She looks exactly as she did the day I told her about my bus ride through Georgia. I open my eyes, the mansion disappears and I start up the hill toward Amsterdam Ave.

The sounds are different too, I realize. The soft cadences of Spanish have replaced the lilt of English in an Irish key. I imagine that the murmur of Yom Kippur prayers no longer falls softly on the early autumn air from black-clad women on folding chairs. The absence of children's voices is striking and I look at my watch. School has been out for a while and yet no little girls sit giggling on stoops. I don't see one game of stickball played in the street nor a single game of four square on the sidewalk. The hum of intensified bridge traffic is the continual soundtrack, human voices an occasional grace note.

A bodega has taken over the space where Mr. O'Halloran used to run his luncheonette. We all bought soda water for two cents there when we didn't have a nickel for a coke. Now the window is filled with statues of Mary and the other saints. The dry cleaners where Mother worked during the early days of the war ("which war," my students ask me, though to me it is always just "the" war), has given way to a *panadería*. A *pan dulce* sounds good and I move to cross the street but as I reach the curb, I almost, by instinct, sit down on it. In my mind's eye, I see Dorothy sitting on the opposite curb. We both wave across the vast expanse of the city street, not yet allowed to cross by ourselves. As I walk toward the shop, I look in vain for a sign in the window that says, "English spoken here." I don't need them to speak English--how much Spanish do you need to buy a *pan dulce* anyway?--but I remember when signs that read "*se habla español*" started to appear on St. Nicholas Avenue.

I go in and begin to search the display case, when I spot a little girl sitting at a card table near the back of the shop. She's bent over a book--some kind of school book--so engrossed that she doesn't look up when the bell over the door jingles. I can't take my eyes from her; her intense concentration is riveting. Her mother speaks softly, "It is my daughter. She is a good student and does her homework as soon as she comes home from school."

Maternal pride is evident in the look she gives her daughter. And suddenly it is my mother's look I see on her face. The little girl had looked up at the sound of her mother's voice. She isn't blond and freckled and Polish, but her eyes--brown, not blue--hold a look I recognize: appraising but hesitant, with a touch of mischief. I've seen it in the mirror.

"Where does she go to school?" I inquire.

"*L'encarnacion*," she replies. Then I notice the uniform, hardly changed after almost sixty years. The little girl smiles and the sense of identification is gone. "Go for it," I tell her in my mind. "Study and dream big. You can do almost anything you want." I buy my sweet and walk out. I used to buy halvah next door but never mind.

What I miss most as I walk along the street is a view of the river. From the mansion's yard, perched on the top of the cliff as it was, we had had a sweeping and unimpeded vista of the Hudson. The wider world was laid out before our eyes and the river's flow beckoned, though we didn't understand how it was working on us. Eventually we would all venture forth.

Tootie had moved to Chicago with her Joe and the baby even before I left for college. Marilyn moved downtown from CCNY, having made herself a small but satisfying place in the fashion industry. We were on each other's Christmas card list and kept in desultory contact. Parents followed their kids as they moved out and up or invested in the new developments on Long Island, pocketing their share of post-war prosperity.

I walk the shrunken piece of Haven Avenue for an hour or so more. I have to admit that the new apartment houses are attractive and very well maintained, I wonder if they have roof access. Do neighbors still meet up there for impromptu parties? Watch parades on Riverside Drive from there? For that matter, are there still parades on Riverside Drive? Do little girls still listen there for the footsteps of a father returning from the war? If I go up on top of one of them, the one farthest to the south where our apartment had stood, will I hear my father's distinctive whistle echoing there? The one that says I'm really and truly home?

All in all, I have to admit that Haven Avenue has, to some degree, bettered itself. Just like most of us who had lived there in the nineteen forties and fifties. Nonetheless I pity the kids who live on this new Haven Avenue for losing the river. I try to take in every detail of the renovated block, but the world of my Haven Avenue keeps pushing in, shoving aside the reality in front of me. It had been such a very different time. That's when I decide that I have to try to remember it all.

1

A Morning Treat

IT'S STILL DARK, mostly. There's only a little bit of light coming in the bedroom window, but I think that maybe the milkman has been here already. No matter how early I wake up, the milkman has already come.

I creep out of bed as quietly as I can so Mommy won't hear me. Tiptoeing across the living room, I stop and listen hard. Mr. Murphy opens his door across the hall. Then it closes and I hear his footsteps down the hall. He's a policeman and he has to take a real early subway to work.

Then someone starts banging on the radiator pipes. It's probably old Mrs. Callahan upstairs. It's only September and the Super won't turn the heat on for a long time, but Mrs. Callahan still bangs on in hope. I listen to see if she woke Mommy up, but everything is quiet in our apartment.

I creep over to the front door, turn the lock and open the door. There are the milk bottles, right outside. I drag one in and close the door again. I can't really lift the bottle by myself so I kneel down and unwrap the paper covering. I do it carefully because I use these milk bottle tops in my doll house--if I put the cover, all folded as it is, on an empty spool after Mommy has used up the thread, it makes a dining room table with a tablecloth. Then I pull up the small lid inside and there it is--the really good cream on top. I bend over, put my lips on the top of the milk bottle and suck it all in.

2

Running Away

I'M GOING to run away. Then they'll be sorry. I thought it would be fun here. Wasn't it fun last time? I'm not sure I can remember last time very well, but I think I had a good time.

I climb up the stairs that go from the kitchen to the bedrooms. Mommy and I sleep in the middle room. My suitcase is in the closet, but I can't carry that. It's too big or I'm too small; I can't figure out which. Anyway, I have a paper bag for my clothes; I found it behind the door in the kitchen. I open the bottom drawer and take out my pajamas and three sweaters. That's all that fits in the bag and that's okay because I don't think I'll be gone long. They'll come find me as soon as they miss me.

I can almost see what will happen. Mommy will notice that I'm not in the kitchen. She'll look upstairs and in the yard. She'll ask Aunt Dee who will say, "I don't know where she is." Then she and Grandma will go down the street and ask all the neighbors. Soon they'll find me and Mommy will say, "Oh, we are so glad we found you! We missed you so much!" And she will take me in her arms and Grandma will say, "I am so sorry I ignored you. You are the best girl in the world."

Grandma doesn't like me. She just ignores me or tells me to go away and play and says she's had enough girls of her own. I thought Mommy would take my part but she just laughs. And she talks more to Grandma than to me. At home, she plays games with me. Here, at Grandma's house, she tells me to find my aunt to play games with. Aunt Dee hates it when I try to find her. The day we came I found her trying on Mommy's hat. She thinks she's grown up and too big to play with me, but she's only thirteen and I heard Grandma say she was getting too big for her britches. She must be dumb if she bought the wrong size. Yesterday, she said she'd show me something in the basement. She led me into the coal room, turned off the light and ran away. I didn't cry but it was hard not to. And I got scolded for getting my dress dirty with coal dust. That's when I decided to run away.

I know Mommy and Grandma are in the canning kitchen in the basement so now's a good time. I drag the bag of clothes down the stairs and then, near the back door, I stop. Where can I go? If we were home, on Haven Avenue, I could go to Aunt Rose's across the street. She would hide me and feed me pierogi. She's not my real aunt but better. It's summer and if I were home, I could go down to the strange, empty house on the corner and hide in the yard. There's a big iron fence around it, but the boys have bent back a piece in one corner where we can slip in. But I don't know anybody on this street and I don't know how to find the path to the creek by myself.

Then I think of the parlor. Nobody goes in there, not ever. I open the parlor door as quietly as I can, but I can hear the voices from the basement so I'm not too worried. It's dark in the parlor but pretty soon I can see a little bit. I look for some place to hide and decide to go behind the couch. I drag the clothes with me and scrunch down as small as I can.

I look around the almost dark room. There are windows in the corner and Mommy says they put the Christmas tree there on Christmas Eve, but I don't think I've ever been here for Christmas. Then I notice a table in that corner with a big candle on it and suddenly I remember. A long, long time ago, maybe last winter, they put Grandpa in his coffin in the parlor. Everybody came to drink and say prayers and kiss all the family. I didn't like the kissing part because all the men had scratchy beards. And Uncle Joe said he'd give me a nickel if I kissed Grandpa and woke him up. I really wanted that nickel, but Mommy held onto my arm and wouldn't let me try. Everybody laughed but I didn't know why they were laughing.

I think about Grandpa in the coffin. Maybe his ghost is still around. I listen really carefully. I think I hear a creak, like somebody stepping on the floor. It's just a little creak, but a ghost wouldn't weigh much or make a big sound. I think I hear a sigh. I'm a little bit afraid, just a little bit. But then I think that Grandpa was sick for a long time and suffered a lot for his sins. That's what everybody said. So probably his ghost is in heaven with the Holy Ghost, a ghost who became a saint.

Just to be sure, I decide to say a prayer. "Now I lay me down to sleep." No, that's for bedtime. "Our Father, who art in heaven. . ." I know my prayers better in Polish, but since I started first grade this year, I had to learn them in English. I finish the prayer and sit some more.

I'm there for hours and hours and nobody comes. I get cold and don't want to sit still anymore. I haven't heard any noise but I bet they're all running down the street looking for me. Mommy's probably crying and I don't want her to cry. I get up, grab the clothes bag and drag it back into the kitchen. Nobody is there and no voices come up from the basement. I look out the back door. Mommy and Grandma are sitting under the grape arbor. They're drinking iced tea and talking and laughing. They didn't even know I'd gone. They don't miss me at all. Tears come into my eyes and I try hard not to cry 'cause I'm not a baby anymore.

I hear Aunt Dee laugh behind me and the tears are gone. I turn around and she's standing at the foot of the stairs. She points at me and says, "What a baby. You don't even know how to run away."

I go past her and up the stairs. This morning I saw a great big spider spinning a web in the corner of our bedroom. Aunt Dee hates spiders.

3

Playing in the Street

DADDY'S HOME on a vacation from the navy. He went to boot camp and then he had to go to school to learn to cook. That seems a funny thing for a sailor to do, but I guess there has to be cooking in the war. Anyway, now he gets vacation for one whole week. And he says I get to play in the street by myself. When it's just Mommy and me, I have to wait till she's ready to go down and sit outside to watch. But mostly she wants to go to the park where there are benches and she can talk to Mrs. Greenberg. But Daddy says I'm getting big now and I have to learn to be responsible, so I can play out all by myself.

The first day he takes me down and tells me I must stay always on our own side of the street. And I do. But when I go upstairs again, I tell Daddy that all my friends live on the other side of the street, Dorothy and Tootie and everybody. So the next day, he takes me down and teaches me to cross the street, how to look both ways, and make sure there is no traffic before I cross.

Last night, when I went up to supper, Daddy met me at the door and he wasn't smiling. He said I was late for supper for the second night in a row and if I was late again, I couldn't play on the street anymore. I said I didn't know when it was time for supper.

"Could someone ring a bell," I asked, "like they do in kinder-garten so we know when it's time for recess and lunch?" Daddy didn't think anyone on Haven Avenue would start ringing bells.

This morning, after breakfast, Daddy says, "Get your coat on, Ninny, we're going for a walk."

'Ninny' is Daddy's special name for me. When my cousin George was little, he couldn't say Annie very well and he called me Ninny. So now Daddy does too. When other people in the family do, I don't like it very much, but when Daddy says it, it sounds all right.

"Where are we going, Daddy?"

"You'll see in a few minutes."

We walk all the way to Broadway and down the street until we come to a jewelry shop. We go in and I wonder why. The salesman calls out from somewhere in the back, "Be with you in a moment."

Daddy and I look through the glass at the pretty rings. Daddy asks me to help him choose one for Mommy. So that's why we came, I think to myself.

"You and I will dream about this ring, Ninny, but we won't tell Mommy about it. When I come home safe, after the war, we'll buy it for her. Till then, it'll be like a good-luck charm for the two of us. Do you think you can keep the secret?"

"Sure," I say. "I love secrets, Daddy. And I'm a big girl now."

"I know you are, Ninny."

Just then, the salesman comes out. "How can I help you?" he asks.

"My daughter needs a watch so she'll know when to come in for supper. She's falling into bad habits."

The salesman looks at Daddy kinda funny, but then he asks to see my wrist.

I have to stand on my tiptoes to reach it up and over the counter. He and Daddy talk about watches and the salesman shows Daddy two or three. Daddy decides on one, and the salesman says Daddy made a good choice. The band is made of small black cords and he can easily cut it to size. He asks to see my wrist again, measures the watch around it and goes into the back room.

It doesn't take him very long and when he comes back he puts the watch band carefully around my wrist and snaps the clasp closed. I turn my arm this way and that, looking at the watch from every side. It has a face with all the numbers on it and two small hands. The face is covered with glass and there's gold around the outside. The clasp is gold too.

"Do you like it, Ninny?"

"Oh, yes, Daddy. I really, really like it."

Daddy gives the salesman some money and they shake hands. Then we start home.

"Now, let's make sure you know how to tell time properly, Ninny, What time does Mommy serve supper?"

"Five o'clock."

"So what time should you come upstairs in order to be ready for supper?"

"Ummm. I guess about fifteen minutes to five. I have to wash my hands and usually I have to go to the bathroom by that time too."

"Okay. Right so far. Now what does the clock look like when it's fifteen minutes to five?"

I think and bite my lip and think some more. I'm sure I know this. But I just can't think of it.

"Shall I run through it all again, just for review?" Daddy asks.

"Yes, please. I think that would be a good idea."

Then Daddy says what the little hand points to and what the big hand points to, how when the big hand is on the left side, from 6 to 12 going up, it shows the minutes before the hour and when it's on the right side, going down from 12 to 6, it shows the minutes after the hour. We practice with make-believe times all the way home. It's a lot to remember.

When we get home, Mommy admires my watch and tells me all the things I have to be careful of when I'm wearing it. More stuff to remember. I can't wear it when I take a bath and when I'm wearing it outside, I can't play in the dirt in the old mansion yard.

"Can I wear it to school?" I ask.

"May I," Mommy corrects.

"May I wear it to school?"

"We'll see."

I hope the answer will be yes. I want the other kids to see I have a watch.

"You're not to be a show off about this watch, Anushka," Mommy says, in her "I-mean-it" voice. Sometimes Mommy hears me thinking. Then she helps me take my watch off and put it in the top drawer of my dresser. Mommy says I won't need it today. We'll all be together and she and Daddy have watches.

We have a big day planned. It's Daddy's vacation so he gets to choose and he wants to go to the Bronx Zoo. He and I really like to see the giraffes. It's funny how Daddy likes all the same things I do.

4

The Iceman Cometh

THE HEAT RISES up from the sidewalk and makes the air wavy. We sit on a stoop in the only bit of shade there is, under a scrawny apple tree, and watch old Mrs. Grady hobble down the street. We can hear cars rumbling onto the bridge above and Mrs. Grady's stick as she scuffles along the pavement—bump, swoosh, bump, swoosh. Then a lazy clip-clop, clip-clop catches our attention. "The iceman," we shout, and in a few moments a cart, drawn by a scrawny gray horse, comes around the corner. Ever since the war started, the iceman drives a horse and wagon.

Now that I think about it, I wonder why the iceman's still around. Since the war started, most of the daddies are gone, even Mr. Green from the grocery store. Mrs. Green runs the store now. The boys say they like it. They don't get so many spankings. But I get tired of so many mommies bossing us girls around.

We know the iceman has only a few stops to make on Haven Avenue. Only three people at number 219 still have iceboxes and one across the street at 224. But at least two of those apartments are on the fifth floor. We look at each other; there's just time enough if we're quick.

We stay on the stoop while the iceman wrestles a large chunk of ice into a burlap sling, drags it to the end of the cart, jumps down and pulls the sling and ice onto his shoulder. He grabs his tongs and makes his slow, bumpy way to the apartment entrance. We count slowly, "One, two, three, four, five, six, seven, eight, nine, ten." Then we jump up, but before we can run down the street to the cart, three large, threatening *boys* come 'round the corner and jump onto the cart. They grab the iceman's pick and begin chipping ice, grabbing up the biggest chunks and stuffing them into their pockets. They shoved the smaller bits with their feet toward the end of the cart where all the younger children had been crowding around. Marilyn scoops the leftover bits into her hands and Tootie tries to shove in beside her.

I stand back for a moment. I don't want dirty bits. I want a big, clean chunk, just chipped off the block. I run around to the front of the cart, step onto the running board of the cab and scramble up the slats of the cart on the side. The blocks of ice at the back of the cart are piled higher than my head. I scramble over them, slip, slide over them, bumping my head as one hand slides out from under me. Tommy Brady—Bratty Tom, we younger girls call him—looks up as I bang into him and, still holding the pick, glares meanly at me. I glare back. Locked in a staring contest, we stand there as precious seconds tick away. Then Tom grins, hands me a large chunk of clean ice, throws down the pick and jumps off the cart and away. I look proudly around only to see that everyone is scattering to the safety of apartment halls. The iceman is in the apartment house door, starting toward the cart as he bellows, "You damned trashy kids get away from my cart!"

As I jump off the back of the cart, I twist my ankle. But I run toward 226, trying to ignore the pain. A girl who won a staring contest with Bratty Tom Brady can't afford to limp.

5

Henry Hudson and Me

I LOVE the smell of hot blacktop when big summer raindrops start to sizzle on it. You can smell the dust cooking and you start to hope that maybe it really will rain and then you will get cool. Not today, though, please don't let there be rain today, I pray. I think God probably has that under control already; I prayed that same prayer all during Mass. Besides, what kind of baby has to stay indoors during summer rain? It's always over quicker than it begins.

Marilyn and I meet at the corner to wait for the gang. She hops from one foot to the other, as if she's gonna pee in her pants.

"What's the matter with you?" I ask.

"I wanna get going," she says. "I'm afraid my mother will come after me and make me stay home. Nonnie's coming to dinner."

Finally I see Mr. Wagner turn the corner and come toward us. The other three kids are with him.

It was all Mr. Wagner's idea. We would walk across the George Washington Bridge and whoever made it to the other side, to Jersey, would get an ice cream cone. Mr. Wagner said that, for sure, they made better ice cream in Jersey, 'cause the cows were right there close. Since I've never seen a cow in Manhattan, even in Central Park where I've seen polar bears, I think he's probably right.

Mr. Wagner makes us line up as we climb to the sidewalk that goes across the bridge. On the way, he gives instructions. He tells us we can't lean over the rail and stuff like that. But he doesn't have to worry. The stupid boys who try dumb stuff like that aren't invited today. Mr. Wagner banned them from this expedition--that's what he calls it, an expedition--because last time they ganged up on Sally and made her fall and skin her knee.

We're moving farther out over the water now and we walk right into a good breeze blowing downstream. Pretty soon all the sweat on my neck and in my hair dries and I'm feeling pretty good. Mr. Wagner says it's time to pick up the pace. It's a mile across and a mile back and he doesn't want our parents to worry about us. I'm not really listening to him, though. It's the kind of stuff grown-ups are always saying. "Be careful, slow down, hurry up, you mustn't make us worry, that's too dangerous, only boys do that, that's for when you're grown-up."

Every once in a while, I feel the bridge sway in the wind. Finally we're at the end of New York. Right in the middle of the bridge, there's a line. On the left-hand side of the line, it says "New Jersey" and on the right-hand side, "New York." You can straddle the line and be in two states at the same time. It seems like a trick when you talk about it, but it's just a certain place to stand.

I look down at the river that I can barely see over the top of the rail and squint my eyes almost closed. Marilyn jostles my elbow. "Look," she says, "there's a dayliner going up the river." Tootie jumps up and down like she's on a pogo stick, 'cause she's too short to see over the rail, even on her tip-toes. She shrieks something too, but I don't pay attention. I'm not on the bridge anymore. I'm on the prow of Henry Hudson's ship, the Moonbeam or something, seeing this country for the first time ever. I light my pipe and nod wisely to the captain. Yes, sir, I think we have discovered a very beautiful country. I know I'm the first person ever to see the beautiful palisades, without the Ferris wheel on top. Then Indians begin to shoot at us and I step over beside one of our big guns.

Marilyn pinches me real hard on my arm.

"Ouch!" I yell. "What did you do that for?"

"Look," she says. "They're way ahead of us. Come on."

I look over my shoulder and see Mr. Wagner is yelling and waving for us to hurry.

Finally we're on the other side. The ice cream is really good today. Mr. Wagner says that means the cows are happy. I am, too. I get peach, my favorite flavor this year. On the way back, Tootsie licks her ice cream off the cone and it plops on the sidewalk in front of her. Marilyn and I offer her licks off of ours before Tootie can start wailing. Tootie wailing can ruin an entire Sunday. The way home seems longer than the way across. Henry Hudson has sailed farther upstream, out of my view now.

6

Sex and the Double Decker Bus

THE TOP of the double-decker downtown bus is one of my favorite places in the world. If I look quickly down the alley of a big street I can see the river for just a second. When we turn onto 125th Street, we drive along Central Park and I can look down on the trees and see kids on bicycles. There's ducks on a pond there, too, and huge rocks. Mommy says the glaciers left them there hundreds and hundreds of years ago. Or maybe thousands. I'm not sure.

Mommy doesn't like riding on the top of the bus because it's open to the sky. She screws up her face, even when it's sunny out, because she hates the wind in her face. I love it. I stick my chin up as far as it will go so that I get as much wind as possible. I like it even though it tangles my hair up bad and I'll yell when Mommy combs it out tonight. She always says, "Stop yelling. I told you the wind would tangle your hair, but you wouldn't listen. So be quiet and take your medicine."

Mommy gets cold a lot. We argue over when it's cold enough for a sweater. It's the same argument every time. "Put your sweater on." "I'm not cold." "But it is cold. Put your sweater on." "I don't want to." Daddy hates it when we argue. Before he left for the war, he took me out for a walk and an ice cream cone. Walking home, he told me that a sweater was something I have to put on when Mommy gets cold. I tried to tell him that didn't make sense, but he put on his we're-not-going-to-talk-about-this face so I shut up. And I'm wearing my sweater, but it doesn't stop the lovely wind from blowing my hair all about.

When the bus stops in front of the Museum, we get off. I'm so excited that I tell Mommy that I have to go to the bathroom right away. I love the museum. It's full of wonderful things. My favorite room is the one full of armor, but we don't start there. I like to keep it for last. We start in the Egypt room. I go looking for the mummies. They have some, but they're inside funny shaped boxes painted all sorts of colors. I keep looking, hoping that someday they'll open up one of the boxes and show us the real mummy inside, but it hasn't happened yet. They have statues of dogs and cats. The dogs wear jewelry and Mommy says they worshipped the cats. The Egyptians were strange people, but their stuff is fun to look at.

Then we visit a room that Mommy likes. When we visit the Museum, we take turns: a room for me and then a room for her. She likes the fake rooms with furniture. Well, the furniture is real but they're not in real rooms. I asked Mommy once if the people who run the museum get to live in the rooms, but she said no. Too bad. It's a job I might want to do one day if I could live in some of those rooms. It's kinda boring, but Mommy likes it a lot. She talks about the furniture, how it's Looey this and Looey that. But her favorite piece this time is a dining room table. She says it's a Dunkin Five table, but it only has four legs, not five. I counted them. Mommy says if she ever gets rich she wants a Dunkin Five table. I hope she gets one. If I'm ever rich, I'd like one of those mummies. Then I could open the box and see what's inside.

When it's my turn for a room, Mommy asks if I'd like to see a new room today. We have to go down one flight of the big white staircase and then we're in a room full of statues. Mommy says they're very, very old and were carved by the Greeks and the Romans. I look around first before I go close and I see that all the statues are of naked people. I look up at Mommy to see if she's embarrassed, but she's just looking at the statues. So I walk around and look hard at each one. Some of the women have drapes over their shoulders. Some of the men are stretching their arms over their heads or holding large round disks in front of them. They're completely naked except for bits of leaves that cover their bottoms, well, their front bottoms. I check carefully, but there's no man statue without the leaves and I am disappointed. I try to figure out what's behind the leaves but I can't get a really good look. I think about asking Mommy but decide that's not such a good idea.

Then it's time to go. Today's really special because we get to go to Woolworth's and sit at the counter. I'm going to have a hot fudge sundae. Mommy always gets a black and white soda, vanilla ice cream and root beer.

On the way home, we sit on the lower deck of the bus. I've had lots of treats and don't want to be greedy. About half way home, Mommy picks up my hand and turns to look at me.

"Let's talk about the statues," she says. "We don't usually go looking at naked people so I suppose you're wondering why people would carve those statues."

I'm really wondering what's behind those leaves but I don't say anything. Mommy tells me how artists always want to make pictures and statues of beautiful things and that the most beautiful thing God ever made was the human body, so some artists try to show that beauty. And it's a good thing for artists to do even though it's not a good thing to run around naked. She asks me if I understand and I tell her I think so. I know that God only makes things that are beautiful and good; I learned that in religion class. But I still wish I could have seen the beautiful thing behind the leaves.

As the bus slowly takes us home, I keep thinking about bodies. I like mine. I like to dance and do cartwheels and hang upside down on the monkey bars and feel the wind on my face. I look out the window and watch the people as we ride by. There are some girls jumping rope and I wave but they don't see me. When the bus stops next, I watch a woman get on. I can tell she's going to have a baby because her tummy bulges out a little bit from her jacket. That reminds me of something else about bodies.

I know how babies grow inside a mother's body. Rosalie's mother told me all about it when she was expecting Rosalie's little brother, Jimmy, last year. I'm jealous of Rosalie; I really want a little brother. When Rosalie's brother was born, I asked Mommy could we please get a little baby brother for me. She said that she really wanted to have another baby too, but that we had to wait until Daddy got home from the war. I asked her why. "Wouldn't he like to be surprised?" I said. She said there had to be a daddy to plant the seed in the mother's body. So I figured that babies were like radishes and grew from seeds. That made a lot of sense.

I imagined Daddy giving Mommy a seed to eat and went looking for a bottle of seeds in the medicine cabinet. That's where they keep important things like that. But there were no seeds there and I thought that maybe he took them with him.

That was way last year. But now that I know more about bodies I'm not so sure about those seeds. I think they might have something to do with what's behind those leaves.

7

A Hard Day's Journey into Supper

DOROTHY and I are playing jacks in the hallway. We've studied our catechism for First Communion class so we get to play until supper-time. The landing on the third floor is dark and we leave the apartment door open to get some light from Dorothy's living room window. We can hear Mrs. Ebersoll in 3C. She's yelling at her son Jack because he got suspended from school and we start to giggle. Then we hear Jack say a bad word to his mother. We can hear the slap through their closed door. I heard Mrs. Ebersoll tell Mommy that ever since his father left for the war, she can't control Jack at all.

We can smell Dorothy's mother, Mrs. Rose, making pierogi in the kitchen. I'm not allowed to call grown-ups by their first names but I'm allowed to call her Mrs. Rose because she's a really good friend, too good to have to call her "Mrs. Staruh," so we've all settled on Mrs. Rose. She stuffs little pockets of noodle dough with all sorts of good things. My favorite is sauerkraut, but I like the mushroom ones too. I really love pierogi.

Mrs. Rose comes to the doorway and asks me to stay to supper. I say that I'd love to but I have to ask Mommy. "Go ahead," she says, "and ask your Mother to come too. There's plenty." I get up, hand the ball to Dorothy and run down the stairs. When I get to the street, I stop and look both ways. Haven Avenue is not a really busy street, but that's what I have to do. I cross the street, run up the two flights of stairs in our building and into our apartment.

"Mrs. Rose invited me to supper and she wants you to come too," I announce.

"How nice of her," Mommy says, "but I hope you didn't beg. I know how much you love pierogi."

"No, I didn't even mention it."

"Well, then, I'd like to come. But tell Mrs. Rose I won't come unless I can bring over some cake I have for dessert." Mommy loves dessert and she bakes as much as she can with the ration stamps. "You tell her that and come back to tell me what she says."

I go back to Dorothy's, stopping at the street to look both ways and running up the three flights of stairs to her apartment. I tell her what Mommy said and Mrs. Rose says, "That would be lovely. Go back and tell her I accept the cake and to please come at 5:00." So I do. Down three flights and up two. Then I come back to play jacks with Dorothy until supper. Down two flights and up three. And I look both ways each time I cross the street.

Mommy comes and we all sit down at the kitchen table. After a few bites of pierogi, Mommy raises her water glass toward Mrs. Rose and says, "To the chef. A wonderful supper is a good reward for a hard day's work."

I want to agree. I surely worked hard for this supper! But my mouth is stuffed full of pierogi.

8

The Window

THERE'S JUST enough light left outside so that I can see the window. It's a big square of gray light in the dark room.

They think we don't hear when they whisper. They think we don't understand. We all stay out late because it's August and there's no school and the apartments are too hot. It's a bit cooler outside although if you stand near the building you can feel the heat come off it. It's like standing in front of the oven when Mommy opens the door to see if the cookies are done.

But we can hear our mother's voices in the dark; they think because we're playing we aren't listening, but one of us is always listening to the mothers. We take turns, then later we share what we hear.

Usually when it's this hot, Mommy lets me fall asleep on the fire escape. She sits with me there till I fall asleep then carries me inside. But not tonight.

Last week, Marilyn heard the mothers say "pushed her up against a wall." I heard "gone away now" and Lizzy heard "no better than she should be." We figured out they were talking about Rosie Wilson; she had indeed gone away, but we couldn't fit the bit about up against the wall into the story.

These last two nights the mothers' voices have changed. They don't say so much but they sound afraid. Two nights ago, Sally heard her mother say "missing" and mine answered "only five years old." Well, that isn't hard to figure out and we all know why our mothers keep us inside today until they can come out with us.

But tonight we all listen. They don't seem to notice that we aren't talking to each other. "In pieces," "in the sewer," "five blocks away," "but not the head."

I'm really tired, but I can't go to sleep. It's way too hot. And, besides, there's the window, right across from my bed.

9

The Recital

I'M in the wings and the big curtains are fluttering around me as we dancers squirm. It smells like dust and face powder and cinnamon, all mixed together. We know not to let our taps make noise on the floor. This is the best--and the worst--moment. I'm scared. I'm always scared just at this moment.

I'm dressed up like Carmen Miranda, with a long skirt that's open in front. It's red satin with lots of stiff ruffles of different colors from my waist to the floor. There's ruffles on my sleeves too. I have big bows and some pieces of fake fruit on my head and bright red maracas that I have to shake in the rhythm of the dance.

I try not to wiggle, not to be scared. There are so many people out there. I peek through the curtain just before we line up and the theater is filling up. I can see Mommy back about ten rows; she's sitting with Great Aunt Celia who came all the way from Jersey City. I hope they're going to give me flowers afterward. That's a theater custom, Mr. Stone says. Everybody in the dance school has lots of family in the audience. And Mr. Stone says that he has invited some people who are experts in this kind of thing. It's big stuff, Mr. Stone says, and we're to do our best. It's a very big audience and they'll all be staring at us.

The rumba music starts. We raise our hands into position and the curtains open. Then we start forward in a line, our taps hitting the beats of the music perfectly. Once we're on stage, we turn to face the audience. But suddenly the magic happens. They all disappear. The big lights block them out and it's as if we're dancing just for ourselves. We start the more complicated steps and movements and suddenly I'm not thinking of anything else, not even the flowers I hope I get afterward. There's just the music and the movement. I'm dancing.

10

A Birthday Present

"SHE'S TOO YOUNG. She's much too young."

"No, she's not. Anyway, it's bought."

I'm in my bedroom, looking at the birthday cards. But I can hear Mommy and Aunt Anna in the kitchen.

"It's too expensive. She could easily lose it."

"I don't think so. Annie's not careless about important things."

"Where will she wear it?"

"To church, of course. On important days. Her First Communion is coming up this year."

"My gosh, Honey, the nuns will never let her wear it. What are you thinking of? They're all in white for First Communion."

"So you'll pin it to her slip, underneath her dress. It's something from her Godmother and it should be part of her First Communion."

"I still don't think I understand why you're doing this."

"A woman must have jewels. Jewels are for the future, when she needs money of her own. Jewels are the only thing she can keep for herself, that she can hide away. I know this. Just in case. For the future. This is only her birthstone, an amethyst, after all. But it will get her started in the right direction."

"But, Anna, she's only seven!"

"It's never too early to start."

"You're thinking of Aunt Elizabeth."

Another aunt! How many of them can there be? Maybe God allotted a certain number to each family and we haven't reached our limit yet. Why have I never heard about her?

"Never mind what I'm thinking about."

"But you are."

"She'd have been able to run away. To start over. To be safe. If she'd had jewels of her own."

To run away? Do grown-ups run away?

I take the pin out of the box and hold it up to the light from the window. It's gold and lacy, kind of like a cobweb, only square. And in the middle is an amethyst. My birthstone. Now I have a jewel of my own. Just in case. For the future.

11

There's a War On

EVERYBODY SAYS THIS. As if there just might be someone who doesn't know it yet. I know about it because Daddy's been gone for over a year now, he's fighting in the Navy.

Mommy says we belong to something called the Home Front and it means that we'll do without things and we have to save things, funny things. One thing the government wants is tin foil. There's tinfoil inside cigarette packs and gum wrappers, the paper that goes around the individual stick. I'm not sure how tinfoil helps the war. I don't think they can make bullets out of it. The boys sometimes make little balls out of it and shoot it with slingshots, but it doesn't really hurt anybody. Maybe, if they get enough of it, they can make a protective cover for the tanks. I can't think of anything else.

Lots of people--they must be really dumb--just toss the packs and wrappers away even though if you save the tinfoil you can get real money for it. Marilyn and I are having a race to see who can get the biggest ball by the end of this month. We don't let Tootie into our race because we found out she rolled a stone in her ball to make it weigh more and that's cheating, so she's banned for life. Now I look down at the street when I walk somewhere and pick up empty gum wrappers and cigarette packs. Mommy hates it. When she saw me doing it the first time, she almost yelled at me. "Put that down," she said. "It's filthy. Come here and let me wipe off your hand." So now I have to be pretty sneaky about it. I miss some when she's looking right at me, but sometimes I can lag behind her and get one that I've just walked over. I stuff them in my purse. Mommy hasn't even wondered why I carry my purse all the time now. I used to just carry it to church.

Something else new in the war is the air raids. They were really scary at first. The big siren blew and everyone rushed to turn off the lights. Then Mommy and I waited in the dark and we could hear Mr. O'Connor yelling, "Youse up there, in the third-floor corner, turn off your lights." It's not so scary now, because nothing ever really happens. When the whistle blew last night Mommy and I listened to Edgar Bergen because you don't have to turn off the radio.

But last week the whistle blew when I was up on the fifth floor playing with the Eder boys. Lots of kids won't play with them anymore because their father came from Germany, but Mommy says that the Eders are good people, they're Catholics and go to our school, and I like Karl and Peter. We play card games and when we play church, I make them let me be the priest and make them the altar boys. They say girls can't be priests and I say that it doesn't matter, it's just pretend, and anyway they really are training to be altar boys so it's good practice. We use white Necco wafers for communion.

When the siren blew, the Super threw the main switch to turn off all the lights so I knew this was a big one. I ran out the door and down the stairs. It was completely dark but I was too scared to be scared of the dark, if you know what I mean. Mr. Eder was yelling for me to come back, but I just had to be with Mommy if the bombs fell. We sat in the dark, holding each other tight until the "all clear" whistle blew. Even though I had Mommy to hold on to, I kept thinking about Daddy. He's where the bombs fall all the time. I want him to come home. I know Mommy wants that too.

Today I'm going to the store and it's Mr. Blackman's just around the corner so Mommy says I'm okay to go by myself. We need a loaf of bread and a quart of milk and that comes to 24 cents. Mommy looks in all her purses, but she can't find a quarter so she gives me a dollar and tells me how to be very careful of it. It's a lot of money. Halfway to the store, I see an empty cigarette pack lying in the gutter on the other side of the street. I look carefully both ways and there's nothing coming, so I start to run across the street. Only I don't see how the manhole cover is sticking up a little bit and I trip and fall, flat on my stomach. I pick myself up and look down at my hands. They're dirty and I don't have the dollar. I look all around and then, just as I see it in the middle of the street, a car turns down our block from 182nd and makes just enough wind to send the dollar flying away. I look both ways again and run down the street after it, but the wind has taken it right toward the sewer and then it's gone. Quick as a wink, I'm there, but it's too late. I kneel down on the grate and try to peer in. I think I see it and I push my arm through, as far as it will go. But it's just an old cigarette pack and it doesn't even have any foil in it.

I sit on the curb for a long time, but I can't think of anything to do, anything that will get the dollar back. I have to go upstairs and tell Mommy.

Mommy doesn't yell too much. It's worse than that. With an angry voice she says, "I told you. I told you to be careful." Then she stops and sits down suddenly on the kitchen chair and starts to cry. She cries really hard. I can't stand it. I throw myself into her arms and we hold each other and cry and cry. Later I go into the bedroom and take out my pennies. I keep them wrapped in my prettiest handkerchief in a silver box, a chocolate box that Daddy gave Mommy the Valentine's Day before he left. I count the pennies. There's thirteen. Enough for bread, but not for milk too. I don't like milk much anyway. I take them to Mommy in the kitchen.

"These are the pennies you were saving to buy a Postal Savings Stamp for war bonds," she says.

"I know. But it's my fault. I lost the bread and milk money."

Mommy waits a moment, then hands the pennies back and says, "No, Anushka, as much as we need bread, the men at war need your pennies more. Keep saving. We'll be all right. We're in this for the duration."

Everybody says that too. It's for the duration. I don't know what a duration is; it sounds like it might be a prize for winning the war. But whatever it is, if Mommy's working for it, I am too.

12

Lunch with the Aunts

"DON'T DAWDLE, ANNIE," Mommy says, as the light on the corner changes. "We don't want to be late for lunch."

We just got off the M4 bus on 172nd St. It comes down Ft. Washington Blvd from our neighborhood and lets us off pretty near the Aunts' apartment. It's really Aunt Anna's apartment, but it's big, practically huge, with 4 bedrooms. Since Uncle Frank went away to the army, two of the other Aunts have moved in. There's still an empty room.

There's a pet store on the corner and I stop to look at the kittens in the window. They're so sweet and cuddly. I really want a pet, but Mommy says we can't right now. Last week she caught a little mouse in a trap and it was still alive. I begged and begged to keep it. I thought we could put it in a shoebox. But Mommy just flushed it down the toilet. I cried for ten whole minutes.

"Come on, Annie," Mommy says and she's starting to get cranky so I hurry to catch up and in no time we're at the apartment. We walk up the five flights and Aunt Anna answers our knock right away. There's hugs and kisses for me and Mommy hangs up our coats.

We go into the dining room and lunch is ready on the table. Aunt Anna has fixed Campbell's tomato soup and toasted cheese sandwiches. They're my favorite lunch and when it's cold and rainy, Mommy walks up to school and takes me to the luncheonette for a hot lunch. We always have tomato soup and toasted cheese. I wonder if Aunt Anna made it specially for me, then I remember it's Friday. We all sit down and I look around.

"Where's Aunt Betty?" I ask.

"She doesn't want any lunch, Annie. She'll join us for coffee and dessert."

Wow. Dessert for lunch. This is something special.

"That woman is too moody for her own good," Aunt Justine mutters. "She'll make herself sick." Nobody pays any attention.

It gets quiet and we all dig into lunch. After the first few bites of creamy Velveeta, I start in on the soup. I try hard not to slurp. I don't want to embarrass Mommy in front of the Aunts. It's still quiet, too quiet. The Aunts are never this quiet. Something's up.

"You start, Anna," Aunt Genevieve finally says. Aunt Genevieve just graduated from high school and came to New York to find a job as a waitress. She found one right away. That's what all the aunts do.

"I'll start," Aunt Justine insists. "Teresa, it's time you and Annie moved in here with Anna and the others."

Mommy puts down her spoon and looks up at Aunt Justine. She opens her mouth but before she can say anything, Aunt Justine keeps talking.

"It makes all kinds of sense. I don't know why you're being so stubborn about it."

"We'd all save money, if you shared the rent and food." Aunt Genevieve says. "My tips are pretty good, but money is still tight."

"I'd love having my goddaughter around all the time," Aunt Anna adds and she reaches across the table to squeeze my hand.

I swallow all the toasted cheese in my mouth at one gulp and look up at Mommy. Oh no, I think. Living with the Aunts. Aunt Anna is wonderful, but . . . . Say something, please, Mommy. Finally she does.

"We've been over this before, Justine. When Edward left. . ."

"And that's another thing," Aunt Justine interrupts. "You should never have let him volunteer. Your husband should have waited until he was called up like everyone else and he never would have been, not with a daughter. But no, he had to go off and try to be a hero."

That's not true. Mommy says he's not a hero, just an American doing his duty. I'm not allowed to brag about him.

"You're just feeling guilty because your husband has been doing everything he can to avoid the draft." Aunt Betty speaks from the doorway. No one had heard her come. "Besides, what are you doing in this discussion anyway? You don't even live here."

"No," Aunt Justine snaps back, "Peter and I are up in Yonkers, living with my mother-in-law. She's old and Peter still has his younger brother to provide for. They need us. I take care of family."

"They need your money," Aunt Genevieve mutters.

"I will not discuss my husband's actions, Justine. That's between him and me." Mommy's voice sounds like when she says "and that 'no' is final, Annie.'"

Aunt Betty sits down at the table and takes a sandwich from the plate in the center of the table. "No, thank you, Honey. I don't want any soup. Anyway, Teresa, there's an empty bedroom with twin beds. It's a shame for space to go to waste during the war. We're supposed to be making sacrifices. That can be yours."

"Wait a minute, Betty. Teresa has made plenty of sacrifices." Now Aunt Anna sounds angry.

"Exactly." Aunt Betty says. "This will be easier on her. Besides, we can have some lovely evenings, Teresa, give each other manicures, do each other's hair." She glances at Aunt Justine. Aunt Justine's bought some beauty shop stuff and is doing perms right in her kitchen for women in her neighborhood. "It'll be just like old times."

"And we could share clothes," Aunt Anna adds. "Think of the savings.'

"Well, that lets me out. I'm several inches taller than the rest of you." Aunt Genevieve is proud of her height and always wears high heels. "But I could baby-sit sometimes, Teresa. You could go out with some friends or with Anna. I'm sure you two old married ladies don't want to go out on the town like Betty and I do, but maybe to a movie? With your husbands away, you can't be having much fun."

"Everybody be quiet," Aunt Anna says, "And let Teresa talk. Talk to us, Teresa. Tell us why you don't want to come. We really do think it would be a help to you."

"Well, there's Annie's school, for one thing."

"I've counted the blocks," Aunt Anna says. "There's only one more block from here to Incarnation than from your place. You can take Annie to school just as easily as you do now."

"But Mommy doesn't take me any more." Finally I have something to say. "I go to school with other kids on the block. We all walk together."

"Annie's right," Mother says.

"What? You let Annie walk to school by herself? She's only in second grade."

"Not by myself," I answer, but Mommy interrupts me.

"We live on a block with very good neighbors. The older children, the sixth and seventh graders, take the smaller ones to school, Annie along with their younger brothers and sisters. That's another reason I don't want to move. We have good neighbors. We watch out for each other."

"That's right," I say, "Why only last week. . . ."

Aunt Genevieve interrupts, "Be quiet, Annie. Children should be seen and not heard."

"What a dumb. . ." I start to say, but Mommy grabs my hand, hard, and I shut up. Aunt Genevieve keeps talking.

"I can't believe you trust young Annie to some other children, Irish kids, I'll bet. Besides the question of her safety, she'll pick up bad habits from those ruffians."

Suddenly I want to defend our neighbors, even Tommy Brady. Mommy just sighs.

"I'm going to the kitchen for cookies and coffee," Aunt Anna announces. The dining room grows quiet as she leaves the room and

I pick up another piece of cheese sandwich. I take a spoonful of soup, but it's cold. The aunts are spoiling lunch.

Aunt Anna comes back with dessert and it stays quiet as we each take our share and start to munch. Then the aunts start to talk about the war news.

Finally Aunt Genevieve asks, "So, Teresa, have you any other objections to staying here?"

"Well, there are Annie's dance classes to consider. We can walk to the studio and it's easy for me to work as the receptionist to pay for her classes. I like being around all the dancers and teachers."

"You spoil that girl rotten," Aunt Justine says.

I start to protest, but the last piece of cookie goes down the wrong pipe and I gag and cough. Mommy tells me to raise my arms and she bangs me on the back. Aunt Betty pours water from the pitcher into a glass and Aunt Anna runs to the kitchen for honey. I'm all right, really, and things calm down soon enough. When they do, Aunt Betty says, "Since you finished your cookies, Annie--rather noisily at that--come with me to my room. I've something special to show you." She puts out her hand. I want to stay and defend Mommy, but Mommy says, "Go on, Annie."

It's pretty special to go to Aunt Betty's room. She always keeps it locked and even Mommy hasn't been inside. It smells all perfumy, like old roses mixed with dust. There's a wind-up victrola, just like the one we have at home, on the corner of her bureau. She puts on a record and sits on the chair by her dressing table. I just stand there.

The music is all dreamy and sad; I grow sad just listening to it.

"Do you know what the song is, Annie?"

I shake my head.

"It's called, 'If You are But a Dream' and it's based on some piece of classical music. It was the song that was playing when I kissed Uncle Michael good-bye. I play it all the time."

He's not my uncle yet, but he and Aunt Betty are engaged, so he's as good as. She's been a waitress down on Wall Street since she graduated from high school two years ago. That's where she met

Uncle Michael. I see a tear on Aunt Betty's face and walk over and put my hand on her shoulder. It's scary when grown-ups cry.

Aunt Betty looks up at me and shakes herself.

"There, I've made you cry. There's nothing to cry about. Michael's going to be fine. Go sit on the bed."

I do as I'm told and Aunt Betty takes a drawer out of her dressing table and brings it over to me. It's full of beautiful scarves and she dumps them out on the bed. There are scarves in every color of the rainbow. There's a red one with yellow trim. There's one that is blue on one edge and then gets lighter and lighter till on the other end it's almost white. One is bright red with large white polka dots. Aunt Betty almost always wears a scarf, sometimes around her head in front of her snood. When she wears a red one, it makes her brown hair have red sparkles in it and her green eyes look even greener. She's almost as pretty as Mommy. No wonder Uncle Michael wants to marry her. As I look at the pile on the bed, I think she must have a different one for every day of the year.

"Pick one, Annie. Whichever you like. It's a little gift from me."

It takes me a long time, but I finally choose one. It's blue-green, all wavy like water, and it has sea shells on, in different shades of blue-green. It reminds me of Rockaway Beach where we spent a week with the Eders last summer.

"Are you sure, Aunt Betty? It's very pretty and you might want to wear it again."

"It's for you, Annie. It will make your beautiful blue eyes shine. Wear it in good health."

"Thank you. Thank you so much. You know I pray for Uncle Michael every night. I pray for all our men who have gone to war."

"I know you do. Thank you, Annie."

Mommy's at the door. "It's time to go, Annie."

WE'RE ALL the way at the corner before we start to talk. I want to ask Mommy about going to live with the Aunts, but I'm afraid of the answer. Finally Mommy starts.

"Well, what do you think, Annie? About living with the Aunts?"

"Have you made up your mind, Mommy?"

"No, Annie."

Good. There's still some time, but I have to be careful.

"It's very nice of them to ask us," I say.

"Yes."

Does she really want to go, I wonder?

"I like Haven Avenue. I'll miss everybody if we move." I cross my fingers. "Everybody" includes Tommy Brady and I sure wouldn't miss him.

"That's true and I'll bet you'd miss Mrs. Rose's pierogis even more."

"You'd win that bet." We both laugh.

"Aunt Betty was very nice to you."

"Ye-e-es. She gave me a very pretty scarf. Still . . .”

By now we're at the corner and I can see the M 4 bus coming along. After we board and get settled in seats near the back door, Mommy asks, "Wouldn't you like to live with your godmother? In spite of what Aunt Justine says, Aunt Anna spoils you even more than I do."

"That's just it," I burst out, "Aunt Justine is always so mean to you."

Mommy waits a whole block before she answers. "She's my sister, Anushka, and not even a full year younger than me. I think she's never quite forgiven me for being born first."

I look at Mommy. She just told me a very grown-up thing and didn't say, "Don't criticize your elders."

"Anyway," she goes on, "Aunt Justine doesn't live there."

I decide I have to try to say a grown-up thing back. "I don't really have a good reason, Mommy, but I like it the way it is, just you and me. Even though you get cranky sometimes and I get stubborn and talk back, it still feels peaceful or kind or something. But when the Aunts are all together, it's different, and I don't like it."

Mommy's quiet for a few more blocks, then she looks over at me and takes my hand.

"Then that's the way it will be, Duchess. You do understand that the money will stay tight. There won't be many treats?" I nod my head.

"Good. I like it best this way, too. We'll get along just fine on our own, you and me."

I relax and give a big sigh.

The bus stops at our corner and we get off.

13

September Questions

ROSALIE IS MY FRIEND—SORT of. We don't go to the same school and we don't play together all that often because church ruins the weekends for us. She goes on Saturdays and we go on Sundays, which doesn't leave all that much free time. Also, she can't come to supper with me on Fridays—the only day that I can have guests during school time. And that's too bad because Mama often makes potato pancakes on Fridays, with sour cream and homemade applesauce full of cinnamon, and Rosalie really likes potato pancakes.

We've gotten to know each other at the dance studio. We both take lessons at the Arthur Braun Studio up on St. Nicholas Avenue. We're in different classes for tap and ballet but together for acrobatics. Now I'm good at back bends. I'm not bragging here. Sister Mary Elizabeth, our fifth-grade teacher, says that the virtue of humility means telling the truth about yourself, so that's all I'm doing, being humble. I'm really, really good at back bends. But every time I try to do a hand stand, I fall over sideways. I think I'm going to have a permanent black and blue mark on my left shoulder. After class a couple of weeks ago, Rosalie came over and offered to help and since then we've been working on our drills and our routines together.

But that first day, she reminded me we had once played together in the park. I thought hard, trying to remember back before I was old enough to go to school and suddenly my face started to burn. I remembered running down the path calling, "Mrs. Rosalie's mother, Mrs. Rosalie's mother."

"Oh, I said," trying to smile, "you're that Rosalie."

"Yes," she said and she was smiling too, not laughing at me, just smiling. "You never could remember my mother's name."

"So I called her 'Mrs. Rosalie's mother'." We both laughed.

Rosalie said, "Mother still tells that story and has a laugh over it. That's how come I remembered, I guess."

That had happened at the end of summer and since then we've been walking home from acrobatics class together. But today I am by myself because it's some Jewish holiday and Rosalie stayed home from dance class.

As I get to the bottom of 180th Street where we turn onto Haven Ave, I notice a bunch of kids standing across the street. Tommy Brady is doing all the talking and waving his arms around and everyone else seems to be listening to him. When he sees me coming, Tommy shouts something and the kids scatter. As I cross the street, I notice that some of the women from Rosalie's building are sitting outside. They're not talking to each other, just sitting with their hands in their laps.

It's happened before, I think it has anyway, I mean that the women at the end of the block have a time when they just sit. It's hard to remember exactly when it happens because who pays attention to what grown-ups do? I mean unless they're yelling at you or something. And usually when the women sit outside, they chat and laugh and scold us kids. But today--and maybe last year at this time--they're really quiet. They're dressed all in black too.

I head off down the block after Tootie, who's moving pretty fast toward her building. Her name's really Gertrude, but she hates it so we always call her Tootie.

"Hey Tootie, wait up," I call when I get near enough.

"Oh, hi," Tootie says as she turns around. She tries to look surprised, as if she hadn't seen me coming down the hill.

"So what's going on, Tootie?"

"What do you mean?"

"You know what I mean. What was Tommy Brady going on about?"

"Oh. . ." Tootsie wails and I put my hands over my ears.

"Stop that wailing and tell me." I grab her by the arm and give her a shake.

"Tommy was telling us about the women who sit near the corner. How they mumble all the time and they're not exactly witches but sort of, and they mumble curses and if you get too close, the curses fall on you." Then Tootie whispers, "And he says you're friends with Rosalie and her mother is one of the sitting women and we have to make you stop being friends with her."

When Tootie finally stops for breath, I just look at her. Then I say, "Tootie, I can't believe you're so stupid." Then I turn around and head straight for Tommy Brady's.

When I knock on the door, Mr. Brady answers and I ask to speak with Tommy. Mr. Brady says that it's almost supper time, but I say that it'll only take a minute. I try to give my sweetest smile, but it's hard because I'm clenching my teeth.

When Tommy comes to the door, I give him a quick kick in the shins. He yells and grabs his leg and I say, "That's for trying to tell me who to be friends with." And before he can say anything, I punch him in the arm as hard as I can. "And that's for being an all-around troublemaker. If any of those women do mutter curses, I hope their curses fall on you, Tommy Brady."

Mommy knows that something's wrong as soon as I get in the apartment. But all she says is that supper's on the table. I don't say much while I eat my meatloaf and mashed potatoes. It's yesterday's meatloaf and it's just as good as it was yesterday, but there's green beans too and I have to eat them real slow so I don't gag. I hate green beans. I try to hide some of them under the mashed potatoes, but there's not enough potatoes left.

Halfway through my rice pudding I put down my spoon and look up at Mommy and say, "Something bad happened today." And I tell her everything. When I finish, Mommy is very quiet. She has that look on her face that means she's angry and trying not to be.

"I've tried to explain these things to you before," she says finally. "Some people who are ignorant. . ."

"Like those Brady twins," I say, but Mommy goes on as if I hadn't said anything.

". . . invent wicked stories to explain things that they don't understand. They're too lazy to take the trouble to learn. I don't want you to be like that. I don't want you to be ignorant. At least you didn't accept that wicked story."

"Do you know about those women? Why they sit and everything?"

"I know a little. Your friend Rosalie's mother explained some of their religion to me. She told me that Jews like Rosalie and her family have a special day to remember their sins and ask God's pardon. The ladies wear black because they are sorry for their sins and they sit quietly to think about their lives and say their prayers. They've been fasting since last night too, so maybe they're just a little bit tired."

I think about sins for a moment and I begin to feel a little guilty. "I told Tommy Brady that I hoped curses fell on him. Do you suppose that's a sin?" I hope Mommy will say it isn't, but she nods her head.

"It probably is, but you'll have to speak to Father about it in Confession."

I shudder. Then I ask, "Why do Jews go to church on Saturday? And why do they have to fast so long?"

"Why don't you ask your friend Rosalie?" Mommy says. "I'll bet she'll be happy to explain things to you."

As I lay in bed, I'm thinking about sin. Maybe I can invite Rosalie to come to confession with me. It'd be a lot shorter than spending a whole day being sorry. But then I think that Jews are probably just like Catholics: you're not allowed to go to anyone else's church. Just before I fall asleep I decide that I won't tell anyone what I said to Tommy Brady, not even Father in confession. If it's a sin, then I have to be sorry, just like the Jews are on their special day. But I'm not sorry. He had it coming. I fall asleep remembering how good it felt to hit him.

14

A Window on the War

I SEE him from the bedroom window. He crawls out of the boat and up the shore of the river on his hands and knees. Then he stands up. He's grinning, but it's not a nice grin--it's mean and scary and his huge white teeth stick out and shine in the moonlight. He's got big glasses on and behind them his eyeballs are popping out from their slanty lids. Then I'm not in the bedroom anymore. I'm down by the river and he's got a gun with a big knife at its tip and it's pointing right out at me. I'm so scared that I try to scream. But I can't so I try to run backwards, up the hill from the river to our apartment house. I know I could run better front-wards, but I can't take my eyes off of him. He's getting closer and closer, so I finally turn around and run as hard as I can. I'm almost there when I turn to look over my shoulder and his face is right there, right next to me. I can feel his breath on my face and hear his horrible laugh.

I wake up. I'm taking big gulps of air, but I guess I didn't scream, because Mommy is sleeping right beside me and she doesn't wake up. I lie quietly for a few seconds, slowly feeling safe. I smell Mommy's perfume on her pillow; it's called "Toujours Moi." I see a little light through the window; morning's coming. I look over at Mommy's face on the pillow. When she sleeps, she looks pretty. I think there's a smile on her face. I've kicked off the covers so I pull my feet in and feel my toes getting warm.

I know that man in my dream. His picture's on one of the posters that are stuck up everywhere. He's a Jap. Daddy's on a ship fighting the Japs in the South Pacific and Mommy put up a map in the living room so I know where the South Pacific is.

When Daddy left, I didn't cry very much, but a strange thing happened. I started to get sick whenever I ate something that I thought I liked, especially hot dogs and chocolate. Ugh. One bite of hot dog and I get horrible pains in my stomach and have to throw up. The doctor says that it'll probably get better when Daddy gets home. I wish he'd get back soon. I'd really like to have a hot dog.

I feel safe, but I know that Daddy's not safe. "Please, God," I whisper, "please keep my Daddy safe."

15

The Audition

I REALLY HAVE to go to the bathroom, but I'm trying not to think about it. Mr. Braun says it's really important for me to be here. It's an audition for a Broadway play and Mommy says that I must stand up straight and look confident. Mr. Braun tells us that we should "own our space" on stage and Mommy says that means the same as being confident. But we're still sitting down to hear all the instructions, so I cross my legs tight and think about not peeing. Finally, the lady with all the papers who's giving the instructions calls a ten-minute break and I race to the bathroom. So do all the other girls so I have to wait in line.

Ginger's here too. She's from our same dancing school, but I don't know her very well. Still, we talk together in line. She's really confident and while she waits, she bends and does pliés. I'm afraid to uncross my legs so I don't do any warm-ups.

When we get back to the waiting room, the lady with the papers--I think her name's Miss Scott--calls our names and puts us into groups of five. Then each group in turn gets called into the audition room. Mothers have to stay in the waiting room.

Our group gets called third and we file into the audition room. We're wearing our ballet flats and carrying our tap shoes. Tap is the first thing we have to do, so we quickly put on our shoes and, as our name is called, we each do our routine. I'm so glad we start with tap-dancing; it's my best thing and it's easy to be confident, like Mommy says. There's no music, but I don't mind because I have the rhythm inside me. I finish with three "wings" and they're perfect! Everyone claps. I sit down. Ginger is last in our group. She trips on her last step and doesn't do any wings at all. I feel a little sorry for her.

Next we have acrobatics and I don't feel confident at all, but I try to look confident. I get through the basics and my splits are really, really good, but when I get to the back flip, I panic and then I wobble and then I sit down flat on my behind. I guess I owned my space by sitting down on it. Nobody claps, of course, and Gracie, the girl who went first and did a perfect routine, looks away as I go back to my seat. She's really sweet. Two other girls wobble too and one of them falls like I did, so I think that maybe I'm not so bad. But Ginger is perfect. Acrobatics is her best thing and she finishes with three backflips in a row. Wow! Everybody claps long and hard for Ginger.

The final thing we have to do is recite a set piece. It's a speaking part we're trying out for, so voice is really important, projection and everything. That's what Mr. Braun says. I'm going to recite "The Soldier Boy and the Little French Doll." It's really a dialogue and, when we did it in the recital Jimmy was the soldier, but I know I can do both voices and it makes people laugh when I do the husky soldier voice. I'm not sure it's supposed to be a funny piece, but I like it when people laugh. I do the piece and, sure enough, everybody laughs at my soldier voice, but they clap when I finish so I feel confident again.

When everybody in our group is finished, we troop back into the waiting room and then we wait and wait and wait. There are two groups after ours that have to try out. One girl comes out crying and I start to say something, but Mommy stops me. "Don't notice," she says very quietly in my ear. "It'll just make her feel bad." But I see that Ginger is giggling and she says something to her mother. I wish it were over. I hate the waiting and Mommy says I can have a hot chocolate at Schrafft's with whipped cream on top when it's over. I'm getting hungry and that hot chocolate sounds good.

Finally the last group comes out and Miss Scott follows them. She thanks everybody and says how we all did wonderfully. Then she stops, takes off her glasses, looks out at all of us seriously and says, "I will be calling five girls back for a second stage of the audition process. But I want you all to know that you have great potential. And if I don't call you back for the next audition, I hope you will continue to work hard at your skills and be sure and try again."

Then she puts her glasses back on and looks down again at her paper and calls out, "Eloise Turner."

She looks up and one of the girls raises her hand.

Miss Scott says, "Please return on Monday, after school. Shall we say 4:00?"

Eloise nods and Miss Scott goes on.

"Lizzy Epscott? 4:30 on Monday, please."

Lizzy was in our group and she was pretty good at everything. Maybe not so good as me in the speaking part, but pretty good. I smile at her across the room and silently clap my hands toward her.

"Virginia Higgins. Please come at 5:00. There will be snacks from 5:00 on because of the lateness of the hour."

That's Ginger! She calls Ginger's name. I'm not surprised. Her acrobatics routine was terrific. But she's not a very good tap-dancer and I thought her voice was pretty weak too. I'm trying to be happy for her and not too disappointed, but it's hard.

Now I'm getting nervous. I want so much to be in this show. I know Mr. Braun will be happy that one of us is making it. But I wanted it to be me. Miss Scott has already called two people from our group. Is it too much to hope for, that there could be three?

"Patricia Collins. Please come at 5:30."

There's only one name to go. Mommy reaches over and takes my hand. I guess she knows how I feel, even though I'm trying to sit still and smile.

"Lilly Stein. Your time is 6:00. Those of you whom I did not call, please pick up your resume and pictures from Miss Ingalls at the front desk. Thank you for coming."

Mommy helps me put my sweater on. It's a special sweater that she knitted for me out of white angora wool. When she finished it looked like a white fur jacket and I love to wear it. I wore it today for good luck, but I didn't have as much as I hoped for.

Over hot chocolate, I tell Mommy all the details of my tryout. She says that it has been a good learning experience for me. I found out for sure what I'm good at and what I have to work harder at. I know I found out how it feels not to be the best. It's not a really good feeling.

16

Tommy's Good Idea

TOMMY BRADY finally had a good idea. Most of his ideas are really dumb, like how we should all try to climb up onto the bridge from one of its feet on Riverside Parkway. Nobody ever takes up Tommy's challenges, we're just not that stupid. Well, almost nobody. Last year he challenged Sally to climb the old iron fence that surrounds the mansion at the corner. Now that was *really* dumb because a long time ago, some of the boys pried up the two bars at the back corner and anybody can slip in and out whenever they want. Anyway Sally did climb up, but her dress got caught on one of the spikes at the top and when she reached around to pull it free, she lost her grip and fell down on the other side. Wouldn't you know it, she fell right on top of the old rusty hook meant to hold the gate open in the old days and she tore a big hole in her leg. You could hear her screaming all over the block. The boys got her out through the opening and her mom brought somebody's old stroller and wheeled her off to Dr. Green's. She got fourteen stitches and had to be in bed for two weeks and part of that time was Easter vacation so she really lost out.

Everybody was nice to Sally while she was in bed. We brought her candy and books and Tootie wanted to bring her the homework, but we wouldn't let her. Imagine having to do homework on top of all her troubles! And nobody said how dumb she was to try climbing that fence. I had to bite my tongue to keep from saying it a couple of times, but we all felt sorry for Sally. But that was last year and Sally's all right now. Better than all right, really, because now when she's bored, she limps around a bit until somebody asks to see her scar. Then she gets to tell the whole story over again. It gets better each time.

But this is a really good idea. We're all going to help the president win the election. Tommy said it was his dad's idea. Mr. Brady works downtown in the Federal Building where he keeps the elevators running (I think he works for a man named Otis). It's such an important job that he doesn't have to go into the Army. Tommy tells us that at least once a week. When Mr. Brady isn't at work, he spends a lot of time at the Hall downtown. The Hall is where a lot of political stuff goes on and it's also where some people go to get help. When Daddy's paychecks hadn't started coming after he volunteered for the Navy, Mr. Brady came over to tell Mommy she should go down to the Hall and get some money. Mommy was really polite to Mr. Brady, but she never went. Instead she took a job in the afternoons at the dry cleaners up on 181st. I asked her why and she said that she didn't want to owe any favors to the Hall.

Those were hard days for both of us. I had to go to Aunt Anna's after school, or she came here to take care of me. And I had to stop my dancing classes because Mommy couldn't work at reception to pay for my classes. Mommy worked from 3:00 to 7:00 and when she came home she was sometimes too tired to eat supper. One night I think I heard her crying in bed. But then the paychecks started to come and it was good again. Just Mommy and me, the way I like it, except for missing Daddy.

Anyway, Tommy finally got a good idea and it's about this election. Governor Dewey is running against President Roosevelt. Now everybody loves the President. We all say, "He gave jobs to America. He should keep his." As far as I can tell, nobody cares much about Governor Dewey, one way or the other. Mommy says that the Hall doesn't like him because he went after them. I'm not sure exactly what that means. The Hall's still there and men like Mr. Brady are pretty strong. Mommy says that Dewey's been a good governor, but she doesn't think he should be president. So we're going to help. I haven't actually asked Mommy about this because I'm pretty sure she'd say no. She doesn't like me talking to strangers.

Tommy has told us exactly what to do. The girls are to speak to the women on the street and always be polite. That's rich coming from Tommy Brady. He gives us three sentences to say, all about the war and jobs and how Democrats are on the side of the working man. Tommy makes us say these over and over again until he's sure we have them exactly right. Then we start.

Tommy doesn't know that I have two more things to say. Daddy says that it's always good to have an ace in the hole. I have two aces.

Everything goes pretty well for a while. I speak to six or seven of the women and they smile and pat me on the head. One says, "You're awfully young to be doing this, my dear. Does your Mother approve?" I answer, "We're all Democrats in our family, Ma'am." I don't want to lie and say I haven't asked her. Then Mrs. Lander comes along. She's got seven children and is older than most of our mothers. She's always angry about something too; even Mommy tries to avoid her. But I have to help the President so I grab her sleeve.

"Don't grab at me, child. What do you want?" she says. I say my first line, "The President gave jobs to our fathers. We should help him keep his." Mrs. Landers makes an ugly sound and says that her husband has gotten his job on his own, thank you very much, and that the President had nothing to do with it. So then I say my second line, "We're at war, Ma'am, and we shouldn't change leaders now."

Mrs., Landers looks at me real hard and says that she knows I understand what war is about and that we've been at it three years. "Look up," she says, "see all those stars in the windows. There are too many gold ones. It's got to stop."

I gulp and think hard. Even though I haven't said my third sentence, I think of her seven children and decide it's time to pull out an ace. "Mr. Dewey wants all us kids to go to school for the whole year--no summer vacation. That'd be an awful thing, Mrs. Landers. Think of how your kids will feel."

Mrs. Landers actually smiles, just a little bit. "Never mind how they'd feel," she says, "I'd like it just fine. Three more months of quiet afternoons. It's not like we can take a house at Rockaway Beach like some people around here."

I'm down to my last ace. I try to look up at her like I'm pleading for my life. "Mrs. Landers, don't you know that the President saved baseball? Don't you think that he deserves more time to save everything else?" She looks at me long and hard, then she walks away.

Whew. That was tough. I count on my fingers. Mrs. Landers was my eighth customer. Two more and, at a penny a piece, I will have earned a dime from the Hall.

17

Homecoming

I'M RUNNING up the stairs and I can hear Mommy coming just behind me. She's telling me not to go too close to the edge. I get to the door at the top of the stairs and push it open. There are already lots of people on the roof. I look around wondering if we'll find a place when I see Karl standing in one corner of the roof, the side that looks over Riverside Drive. He's waving both hands to get our attention. Mrs. Eder is standing next to him, holding his little brother Peter tight by the hand. We hurry over.

Karl tells me that they've been there an hour already, saving places. All around us the neighbors are happy and noisy. The war's been over for several months, but everyone is still acting like it's a holiday and today it really is. It's Navy day and we're waiting for a big parade to start down Riverside Drive. President Truman's in town to visit the Navy ships that have docked here.

The day the war finally ended, Mommy and I were at the movies, the Loew's up on St. Nicholas Avenue. The movie was "Anchors Aweigh" and it was all about sailors like Daddy. Mommy told me I could watch Gene Kelly dance and improve my own dancing. Wouldn't you know it? Right in the middle of the movie, I had to go to the bathroom. When I was washing my hands, I heard a lot of noise out on the street. I looked out the window and saw bunches of people out there, not going anywhere, just walking back and forth, cheering and talking. There was a group of girls carrying flags and singing.

When I got back to my seat, I whispered in Mommy's ear and told her I thought something good had happened, but she just said "shush." I didn't want to think that the war was over. Mommy said it would be over soon because we dropped some big bomb on Japan, but I was afraid if I thought it was over, I'd jinx it. So I kept trying to think that maybe it was a big battle that we won. But when "The End" came on the screen, the lights went up and a man stepped in front of the curtain. "Ladies and Gentlemen," he said, "the war is over. Japan has surrendered unconditionally." Everybody jumped up and started cheering but Mommy and I hurried out. We wanted to get home and be with the neighbors.

When we got to Haven Avenue it was full of torn paper and people were throwing more out the windows. It was almost up to our knees. We were still at the far end of the block, when somebody yelled, "Stop, stop, everybody. Stand exactly where you are." We stood. Then the word came down the block, passed from one group to another.

"It's Mrs. Gregory's little boy."

"He's not even a year old yet."

"What did you say? He's dead?"

"No, for God's sake, no, she thinks he crawled out the door and into the street."

"She should take better care of her kids. You can tell she's not Irish."

"She takes wonderful care of her son. You don't know what you're talking about. You Irish are all alike, bad mouthing everyone else."

"Shut up, both of you. Quit talking and start looking."

Mommy and I join everybody in feeling around our feet. Then there's another shout and Mr. Gregory comes out of the apartment building holding Jerry over his head. We all go back to jumping around and cheering.

That was months ago. Last Thursday, Mommy got a telegram; Daddy was in San Francisco and starting home as soon as he could get a train and Mommy got another telegram from every place the train stopped. She won't let me see them and I think I know why. Daddy can get pretty mushy sometimes. The last one said he'd be home today, but he would have to go first to the base on Long Island. Mommy thinks he'll come after dinner so we have plenty of time to see the parade and she made a wonderful cake. She used the last of her sugar coupons.

Now the parade is about to begin. We watch as row after row of our soldiers march by, their backs straight and their lines perfect. When a band goes by, Karl and I sing along and march up and down; Karl pretends he's playing a trumpet. Then we see the sailors come by and Mommy and I cheer as loud as we can. I notice Mommy and Mrs. Eder holding hands and tears are running down Mrs. Eder's face. I know that she has relatives in Germany and hasn't heard from them for a long time. But I think they're happy tears too, because she's smiling just a little bit.

Suddenly I hear a whistle. It's Daddy's whistle. I turn and he's there in the doorway. I blink my eyes hard for a moment then look again. He's still there. He's real. I run to him and jump into his arms. He holds me close and I smell the Daddy smell, cigarettes and everything else that's Daddy. I'd forgotten all about the Daddy smell until now. Now I know he's home for sure.

18

Interlude

I'M SITTING on the end of the bed, watching Daddy unpack his duffel bag. I have to get up for a moment so Daddy can put his pants underneath the mattress. They're folded just like when they hang over the hanger.

Daddy says, "That's how sailors keep their pants pressed with the crease in."

Most of the stuff from the bag goes in the laundry basket. Then Daddy opens the closet door to hang up his pea jacket. He stares inside for a long time, then turns to Mommy.

"Teresa, I've been gone three years and there's only your same old things hanging in the closet."

Mommy laughs. "Of course," she says. "How do you think I kept your daughter in clothes and shoes, especially shoes? I swear her feet grow two inches every six months."

I look down at my feet. Mommy's fibbing, I think. They haven't grown that much.

It's quiet again, so I look up and see Daddy looking at Mommy. He's got a really funny look on his face.

"Tomorrow we go shopping," Daddy says. "You need a whole new wardrobe."

Mommy doesn't say anything. She's smiling, but there's a tear on her cheek. Mommy's pretty. I think I've just noticed how pretty she is.

Suddenly Daddy says, "Off to bed with you, Ninny. Tomorrow's going to be a busy day."

I run to the bathroom and brush my teeth. Daddy didn't say that the shopping trip is for me too, but I'm hoping he thinks about that tomorrow.

I snuggle down in my bed and wait. I can smell that the sheets are clean. Mommy hangs them on the roof and when they're clean, like now, they smell of sunshine and soot. I wait and wait, but Mommy doesn't come to say my prayers with me. I wait some more and listen hard. Mommy and Daddy were talking in the next room, but now everything is quiet. I guess they went to sleep too. So finally I say my prayers to myself. Daddy's been home only a few hours and things are changing already.

19

The Chosen

I CAN'T BELIEVE they chose me! I never get chosen when we play stickball at lunch. The police put up barriers so that we can play in the street and there's two captains who choose up the sides. Sometimes, if enough kids are absent, I get chosen last. But usually someone just says to me, "You can be cheerleader." And it's not because I'm a girl. We're all mixed together for stickball. It's just me. I'm really great at jacks, but with any ball larger than a golf ball, I'm just a klutz. It's hard on Dad. He's so good at ball games that the boys ask him to come out and play stickball with them. He'd really like me to be better at ball games.

But now they've asked me to play football with them. And it's mostly boys who play football. This is my chance to impress Dad. When Billy Gregory asked me to play he said it's because I'm so fast. And I really am. I win a lot of races at school. "Besides," he said, "Jerry has the measles and he usually runs for us. So we thought you could do it." So now I'm running as fast as I can down the hill to Riverside Park. I'm running so hard that Marilyn can hardly keep up. Marilyn insisted upon coming along. She says she'll be a cheerleader for me!

It's a glorious day. Aunt Anna says that New York has three

seasons--miserable summer, miserable winter and October. Today it's October and so beautiful that it almost hurts. I can see the sun sparkling off the river and from this far away you can't see all the junk that floats in it. And I can see our boys gathered in one of the almost-level places.

When I get there, Billy explains what I'm supposed to do. For the first couple of plays, I'm to move forward and try to knock the guys on the other side down. Billy says he knows I'm not very big and they don't expect much help, but to do what I can.

"Before each play," Billy explains, "we huddle together and if I say 'T-6' that means you're to run ahead and try to catch the ball I throw you. If you catch it, you run as fast as you can to the sidewalk. That's the goal line," and he points it out.

We play on for a while and I try to knock the boys on the other team down. Mostly I end up getting knocked down myself, but twice I knock somebody from the other side down and it feels pretty good. I'm getting a little sore, but the grass is soft and I don't mind.

Then in the huddle, Billy says T-6 and I start to feel nervous. It's gonna be my turn to catch the ball. We line up and as soon as Billy gets the ball I start to run forward. I don't start too fast. I want them to think I'm just coming to knock them down. I run kind of sideways so I can keep my eyes on Billy. Then suddenly, the ball's coming my way. I keep running but put my hands up to catch it. For a moment I touch it and it wobbles a bit, but then somehow I grab it and clutch it to my chest with both hands. I keep running and try to dodge in between the boys coming at me. Just as I'm almost at the sidewalk, someone pushes me hard from behind. I stumble forward, take two more steps, then I feel another push and I go down hard, right onto the sidewalk.

The ball pushes the air out of my chest and for a second I can't breathe. Then I can and I roll over. But my left arm is all twisted up underneath me and it hurts. A lot. I bite the inside of my cheek to keep from crying. Most of the boys on our side are cheering, but Billy is bending over me and trying to help me up. When I get up, he squeezes all the bones in my arm, one by one, and when I say they don't hurt he smiles and says that probably nothing's broken but I'd better go home.

Marilyn and Billy walk me home. Billy's very polite and Dad doesn't yell or anything, but when Billy leaves, Dad takes my arm and carefully moves it this way and that. He agrees with Billy that nothing's broken. It's a sprain and Dad fixes a sling for me out of one of Mom's scarves so that it doesn't hurt as much. I try to tell Dad that I made a touchdown, but he doesn't smile. All he says is that I have to pay the price for my fun. Mother's mad. I can hear her banging pots around in the kitchen. Supper's very quiet and after I've cleared the table--with one arm!--Mother says that she thinks I should go to bed early. Because of my arm and all. That means no radio, no "Hit Parade," and that's one of my favorite shows. The fun of that touchdown has already cost me a hurt arm, and now the "Hit Parade."

Lying in bed, I can hear them talking in the living room. Mother keeps saying that Dad has to talk to me about not playing football.

"She's too old for that rough and tumble with boys."

"But she's not yet ten; she'll only be ten next February. There's time yet."

"You like to see her tomboy ways. I think you encourage her."

"I guess I see myself in her, just a little bit, the way she throws herself into things."

Wow. Dad thinks I'm like him. I know I have his blond hair and blue eyes and Uncle Joe calls us 'Pete and Repeat.' But could I really be like him, even though I'm a girl?

"Yes, but she's not your son. She's your daughter."

There's a silence then. I know Mom and Dad really want to have a second child. When I was little, I prayed every night for an older brother. Then I got smarter and now I pray every night for a younger brother. But they're still a little sad that I'm the only one.

"You have to help me teach her how to be a young lady," Mother says.

"That's your job and you're good at it," Dad objects.

"Not good enough. She was playing football in a dress!" Mother's almost wailing as she says that last bit. Just like Tootie wails.

71

"Maybe it's time that you bought her those dungarees she's begging for."

Yes, I think, oh please, Mom.

"Absolutely not. I'll turn her into a lady even if it kills both of us." And finally Mother laughs.

Dad thinks Mother should have the talk. But she says no. "Since you've been home, she hardly pays attention to me at all."

I want to yell out that it's not true, but I'm not so sure. Finally Dad says he'll talk to me.

It's quiet in there now and Dad turns on the radio. I sigh and turn over in bed. I guess my football career's over. But I can just hear the "Hit Parade" as I start to doze off.

20

Something I Don't Want
to Know

THE SUBWAY IS hot and crowded but we're almost there. We all start shoving and pushing toward the door as the train pulls into the station. Tootie steps on some guy's foot and he turns around to shove her back, but Billy's standing right beside her. Billy's big. He plays football. The guy turns back and pushes toward the door. Finally we're up the stairs and into the fresh air.

It's the last Saturday in June and it really feels like summer at last--hot sunshine and no weekend homework. We join the stream of people going into Van Cortlandt Park and head toward the pool. There're seven of us in our group--Tootie, Marilyn, Anita and I with Billy, Peter and Charley. We see another group from our class ahead of us.

In the women's dressing room, the four of us find a corner and begin to change clothes. I try to avoid looking at my breasts as I change. It's not hard; there's hardly anything there. They've bumped up a little bit, but they're still smaller than anyone else's in my class. Even Tootie has bigger breasts than I do and she's six months younger. Mommy says not to worry, they'll get bigger in time. In time for what, I wonder, but I don't bother to ask. Tootie's mother buys *Modern Screen* and we get *Life* magazine, but no matter how hard I look I can't find a movie star with small breasts.

We did find an article that said cocoa butter helps to enlarge breasts, so I bought some and have been rubbing it in every night, but my breasts haven't grown at all. Oh, well, it really doesn't matter so much in my bathing suit. They put stiff stuff in the top so it sticks out all by itself, just as if there were real breasts inside. Tootie and I brought locks so we stuff everything into two lockers and head out to the pool. I pin the key in the top of my bathing suit.

Our crowd heads to the shallow end and we play keep away with a dodge ball until the Lifeguard comes over.

"Hand over the ball," he says. "It's too dangerous for the little kids with you all jumping around like that. You can have it back when you leave. It'll be in the office."

He walks away and we play tag for a while then everybody heads for the deeper water. Everybody but me. I climb out of the pool and sit with my feet in the water and watch.

I don't know why I can't learn to swim. Last summer, after sixth grade, I signed up for lessons at the Y. I did fine at the beginning. I got past being afraid to go all the way under water and when it came to leg kicks, I caught on right away. The teacher said my legs were strong and I kept them straight the way you're supposed to. I told her it was because of dancing lessons. Then I learned to float on my stomach and my back. I kept right up with everybody in the class and again dancing helped. Arching my back when I floated just felt natural. But then, for the last three days of the class, we were supposed to actually swim. To pass the class you had to swim from one side of the pool to the other and I just couldn't do it. When I tried to do the head thing right--face down, then to one side, breathe and back down in the water--I stopped kicking or something. When I tried to concentrate on stroking my arms right, I forgot to move my head sideways to breathe and I choked and went under, hands and legs in all directions. No matter how hard I tried, I just couldn't do it. I failed Red Cross Swimming Class. Dad said I should try again this summer, but I've had enough of that.

So I sit by myself at the side of the pool. Tootie has gotten out too and has gone with two girls from the other group to lie in the sun. I can hear them murmuring behind me. But I'm watching the swimmers. I watch Billy really carefully. I watch how he moves his arms, legs and head. I begin to see that there's a rhythm to it. Right arm up and forward with his face in the water, then he pulls his left arm up and his head goes sideways and he breathes. I notice that he leads with his elbows, instead of lifting his whole arm out of the water, like I do. He lifts his elbow back toward his behind and makes a big circle forward. I start doing those movements in my head, feeling how the body would do it. I try to imitate Billy's rhythm, kind of slow and steady. I'm starting to think that just maybe I could do this.

Then I hear the voices behind me. One of the girls, I think it's Joan, is saying, "She thinks she knows everything," and I wonder who they're talking about. Then someone else says, "She's always got her hand up, showing off."

"Teacher's pet," Joan says.

"Goody-Two-Shoes," someone else puts in.

"She is not," Tootie isn't wailing yet, but her voice is sharp. "She may think she knows everything--well, she knows a lot--but you can't call her Goody Two-Shoes. She's the only girl in our class who had to stay after school in the first grade. The first grade! And when Fr. Desmond gave out the last report cards, he made a big deal over hers. Said he couldn't understand how someone got A's in all the subjects, but C's straight across in Conduct."

"That's true." Joan's voice again.

They're talking about me.

"But she's so bossy. How do you stand it, Tootie? She's not a very good friend to you, always telling you what to do."

"Well," Tootie says, "But she's nice to me sometimes, too. She lent me a dress once, for Anita's party, and last summer she taught me to play gin rummy. My family doesn't play cards."

I sit as still as I can. I want to disappear but there's only the water in front of me and I'm not sure that I can get in quietly. Then Joan says, "Like I said, she's always showing off, her dancing and stuff. But she can't swim. How's that for a laugh."

I sit another few minutes, trying to forget what I've heard, trying to think back to the swimming movements I had practiced in my head. Then I slip into the water and start. Face in the water, right elbow up, face to the left, left arm up. Again, right, left, breathe, kick. Right, left, breathe, kick. I'm doing it. I'm swimming!

But I've got my eyes closed and forget to look. Suddenly I bang into someone and go under, swallowing water. When I stand up again, I start to yell at the boy in my way, but I hear Joan's voice in my head. *"Bossy."* I go back to swimming. Right arm, left, breathe, kick.

I get to the other side of the pool and Billy's there. He gives me a pretend slug on the arm. He looks even happier than I feel. He's a really good friend. He gave me my one and only lesson in football and he's been giving me all kinds of tips about swimming.

"Not a very good friend." I hear Joan's voice again.

"You did it! I knew you could. Race you to the other side?"

I laugh and say, "Thanks, Billy. You're sweet, but I'm not ready to race yet. I have to practice."

"Showing off." Joan's voice.

Billy swims away and I turn around and start to swim back. I go back and forth across the pool until I'm tired.

On the subway home, I stare out the window. But I don't see the dark tunnel walls speeding by or the lit-up stations. In the window I see my own face, with Tootie's face behind it, smaller and anxious. I don't know what to say because I don't want her to know that I heard all that stuff. I make a silent resolution to be nicer to Tootie. Maybe she'll outgrow the wailing "in time." I lean over and whisper into Tootie's ear, "Let's get an ice cream on the way home. My treat. And then I've got a new card game to teach you. Canasta. It's a lot of fun." Tootie looks amazed.

I'm really happy about being able to swim. And I can't wait to tell Dad. But I can't get out of my head what I heard. It makes me feel strange, somewhere between angry and ashamed. Mother always says not to eavesdrop because you're likely to hear something you don't want to know. I hate it when she's right.

21

Nicknames

I REMEMBER THE CONVERSATION. It seems to me we had it more than once.

"Mommy, why do you call me 'Duchess'?"

"Because you act like one. I hope to heaven you marry a rich man. And now that we're on the subject, why do you call me 'Sergeant'?"

"Because you act like one."

We both laughed. It was funny then.

22

The Martyr and the Trumpeter

WE'VE COME DOWN to the Roxy Theater for the Saturday Matinee; it's a movie about St. Joan of Arc. There's not a lot of Catholic stuff in the movies and Mother said we shouldn't miss a rare chance like this. But for Dad and me, there's another reason to go.

And it's just the two of us today. Aunt Anna is expecting her first baby and she's kind of old to be having her first; she and Uncle Frank waited a long time for this and she's pretty scared. She begged Mom to come and, of course, Mother couldn't refuse, no matter how much she wanted to see this movie. She left to take the subway to the Long Island train early this morning. So Dad and I are on our own.

"I'm taking my second best girl to the movies," he says when we go in. "We'll get some popcorn." He buys popcorn for both of us and a box of "Good and Plenty" for me. He knows I love licorice.

Going to the Roxy is like going to a castle. The lobby is huge, with the highest ceiling you can imagine. It's got half pillars stuck all around the walls and a beautiful oval rug that Mother always oohs and aahs over when she comes. Inside, the theater is all red and gold with several balconies and it holds hundreds of people. But the best thing is the orchestra pit that goes up and down. And at special movie showings, some of the Big Bands play here.

"The Roxy is like a church, Dad," I say, "only bigger and more ornate than any church I've ever been in, even St. Patrick's cathedral."

We go inside and find good seats.

Marilyn and Mrs. Murphy saw the movie last week and Marilyn said it was pretty good. She liked the way Joan talked back to the judges and prosecutors. Strong and kind of sassy but not too much. After all, they had all the power and Joan risked everything. I know a little bit about talking back and it's really hard to keep on the right side of the line. Not that it did her much good to be careful. In the end, they burned her at the stake. While she was alive. Ugh. I almost gag when I think about it. She's a martyr, though, and got canonized for her trouble. Now she's Saint Joan, so I suppose it was worth it.

We sit and watch the final credits. I'm trying to remember some of the dialogue between Joan and the judge. It was as good as Marilyn said, maybe better. I'd like to make a trip to the bathroom but I'm afraid the line will be long and I don't want to miss even one note of the band.

"Hey, Dad, have you ever noticed that in the intermission the line at the ladies' room often snakes out the door while there's never a line out of the men's? I wonder why that is? Someone should fix that."

Dad just smiles. Then the house lights go up for a few minutes and, when they dim again, we hear the first notes of the trumpet. Five sweet, slow notes. The band joins in and "You Made Me Love You" gradually gets louder as the band rises in the pit. Then it's one great Harry James hit after another. "I'll Get By" follows "It's Been a Long, Long Time." Dad sang that to Mom and me on the night he got home from the war. We'd had dinner and Mom's special cake, then he came around the table and took both of us in a big hug and sang, "It's been a long, long time."

Next it's "Somebody Loves Me" and a couple of other songs that Dad and I both really like. When they break into "I've Heard that Song Before," Dad looks over at me, smiles and gives me a gentle poke on the head. He always sings that song whenever I promise to do something like wash the dishes or clean up my room. But mostly we just sit back and listen to that sweet trumpet and the wonderful melodies. Harry James has been my very favorite forever and ever.

When the band begins to play "Take the A Train," I take it as a sign that I should go forward with my autograph book. We do take the A train home sometimes and I love the song; I consider it my theme song. I know it was the Duke's song first, and I like that one best, but I like the Harry James' version too. I go slowly down the dark aisle and wait at the pit, really close to Mr. James. All too soon the music stops and Harry James turns around toward the audience for a few words of farewell. I'm there with my book and pencil and without a word he takes them both and signs the book with a flourish. As he hands it back, he gives me a big smile and says, "Thanks, kid, and good luck."

I walk back to my seat as the last bits of music float up from the pit. Wow! I can't believe it. I've just gotten a blessing from Harry James.

Dad agrees that we should take the "A" train home, in honor of Harry James, even though it takes us longer to get home that way because the "A" train's a local for part of the way. We get off at 180th and Broadway and walk along Broadway toward 181st, taking in the shop windows. I poke Dad in the arm and point toward an outfit I've been admiring in Morgan's dress shop. It's a plaid pleated skirt with a cream-colored sweater set. The cardigan has a strip of matching plaid down the front. Dad looks at it carefully, looks back at me, then looks back to the outfit. Then he shakes his head.

"You can do better," he says. "Besides, your mother says we can't spend any more money this month. Our budget for 'extras' is all used up."

"We're window-shopping, Dad. I just wanted your opinion." Then I sing out the first line of "I'll get by."

Dad breaks into a big grin and we turn the corner at 181st and start down the hill. All the way down, we sing the songs from the floor show. We know all the words, because the radio is on almost all the time since Dad came home. Except when I have homework to do.

Mom opens the door almost before I knock and we can smell the meat loaf cooking.

"How was your date?" she asks.

"The best ever," Dad and I answer and we laugh. It comes out exactly together, just like a song.

23

Reading Can Get You Into Trouble

IT'S the first day of eighth grade and I've got butterflies in my stomach. I'm always excited for the first day of school. And the last. The stuff in between can get pretty boring sometimes, but I'm still excited on the first day, even though there's always some teacher who asks the stupid question, "What did you do on your summer vacation?" Sister Henrietta, who teaches eighth grade, is new this year and I don't know what she'll ask. But I hope she asks us about our reading over the summer. I can't wait to tell her. I'm going to start eighth grade with a bang. It's my last year in grammar school and I have my eye on some of the graduation prizes.

Back in the summer before sixth grade, Marilyn and I went to see "The Three Musketeers." It was a great movie. The costumes were gorgeous and the fight scenes had our hearts in our throats. We cheered when Gene Kelly won every fight. We loved how the Musketeers stood up for one another: "One for all and all for one." After the movie, Marilyn and I decided that we'd tell Tootie about it and we'd be the three musketeers of Haven Avenue. Tootie practiced fencing with her mother's broomstick all summer and I drew costumes and wrote new scenes for us to practice. We were such children then.

In July, I went to our library, the Fort Washington branch on 179th St, looking for some new books. Most of the librarians know me pretty well there. I can still remember the day I got my first library card, even though it was eons ago; Mrs. Lincoln asked mother to sign the card and I insisted on doing it myself. I couldn't reach up to the tall desk so Mrs. Lincoln brought me around to the side where her own regular desk was and even though I could still only print my name, she accepted it.

Anyway, I can't find anything I haven't already read in the Young Adult section and wander over into the Adults. Not far into the alphabet, I discover the works of Mr. Alexander Dumas; Mr. Dumas certainly wrote a lot of books--there's a whole long shelf full, some of them in French. I think I'll take French in high school, after Latin--everybody has to start with Latin, I think. Dad says that Spanish would be more practical; there are more and more "se habla español" signs up here in Washington Heights. But I think I'll do French and read Mr. Dumas' French books. I remember the movie and smile.

When I get to the checkout desk, Mrs. Lincoln--yep, she's still around--looks at the book and says, "I'm sorry, Anne. I can't let you take out this book. You're not yet sixteen and I can't allow you to check out adult books."

I try to argue. I'm pretty sure that I never saw that rule written down anywhere. I try to tell her it's for a school assignment, but she's not having it. She keeps track of what the school assignments are, even in the Catholic schools. Besides, it's July. Finally I give up, pick another book and walk home.

After a few days, I decide to try the main library branch downtown. No one knows me there and maybe they'll think I'm already sixteen. Or maybe, as I suspect, there is no such rule. There's no way I'll look sixteen--even when I *am* sixteen because I'm short and have a baby face. But maybe if I wear my Sunday shoes with the Cuban heels. . . .

I hadn't told Mother about trying to check out *The Three Musketeers* so she doesn't know why I want to go to the big library, but she knows it's one of my favorite places so she doesn't suspect anything.

During the War, Mother and I used to go there for a treat. They have the best little kids' reading room in the world and she always let me climb up and pet the stone lions at the front doors. So down I go and, sure enough, I walk out with *The Three Musketeers*.

It turns out to be a bit of a struggle, not as good as the movie. I skip some of the boring bits and hurry on to the fighting. There's a Cardinal in the story who has a lot of political power. He also carries on with somebody called Milady and tries to keep the Musketeers from helping the Queen. I figure that Dumas made up a lot of that stuff, because I know about Cardinals. We have one in New York and, when he's not saying Mass and hearing confessions, he mostly parades around in bright red clothes and tells everybody what movies not to see. You do see him with the Mayor sometimes but he's not in the government like Cardinal Richelieu. I guess that's because we have "separation of church and state" here in America. We learned about that last year in seventh-grade history and after reading about Cardinal Richelieu, I think I know why the Founding Fathers made that rule.

English class comes at fourth period, right before lunch. Sister Henrietta tells us about our two textbooks--one for English composition and grammar and one for literature. Then she talks about the assignments--lots of composition writing--and the expectations--"very high this year, boys and girls. We must get you ready for high school." Finally she turns to the topic of summer reading. That's what she says, actually, "Let us turn our thoughts to the topic of summer reading." I shoot my hand up, but Sister calls on several other kids first. Then it's my turn. I stand up.

"I read *The Three Musketeers* by Alexander Dumas, Sister Henrietta. It was very historical, about France before the Revolution."

To my astonishment, Sister Henrietta isn't impressed. In fact, she looks quite appalled and after a moment says, "But that book is on the Index, Anne. Surely you know."

I stand there, puzzled. All around me are giggles and whispers. I'm not sure what Sister means. I know that there's an index in the back of lots of books, but I never heard about an index that a book could be on. I want to tell her that she must be mistaken, but contradicting teachers gets you in a lot of trouble. So I just start to sit down when Sister says, "That's a serious sin. You'll have to go to Confession." There are gasps all around the room. Mortified, I slump down in my chair.

Lots of girls crowd around me during lunch. They want to know about what was in the book.

"What were the bad parts?" Marilyn asks.

"I don't know," I say. "Maybe there was too much fighting."

"That makes sense," Marilyn says. "There was sure a lot of fighting in the movie. But Father Desmond didn't say anything about not seeing it. The priests tell you what movies are forbidden and they publish a list in the bulletin. And we were much younger then."

"Come on," Joanie says. "There must have been something bad in it. Were there swear words?"

"No, or at least I don't remember any. Maybe it was all that made-up stuff about the Cardinal. His political power and everything."

"I'll bet there was sex in it," June says. She whispers the word *sex*. "They're always trying to keep us from thinking about sex."

"Well, there was some, I guess. But Dumas didn't give any details."

Tootie just keeps patting my hand and looking scared. We've talked about sin before, Tootie and I, and we're pretty sure we've never committed a serious sin. Most of the stuff we tell Father in Confession on Saturdays is venial sin. A serious sin can send you to Hell. I feel just awful. And scared. I'll have to be careful going home, I could get hit by a car and have to go to Hell!

I can't wait to tell Mother all about it after school. I tell her everything I can remember about the book and that I think there wasn't anything very terrible in it. We talk about sin.

Finally Mother says, "I think that you shocked Sister Henrietta and that she didn't think very carefully before she said what she said. You know that you can't commit a serious sin unless you know it's serious and really want to do it anyway. You can't commit a sin just by accident. You learned that in your catechism."

I sit straight up. Of course I know that. I learned it way back in second grade for First Communion. Why hadn't I remembered it when I needed to? Why was it when someone in authority told you something, you were sure they were right and didn't figure it out for yourself? That can't be a good thing to do. If I had thought for a minute, I could have spoken right back to Sister Henrietta and told her she was wrong. Well, maybe not. But I could have said something; I could have defended myself. But Sister had scared me so much--and embarrassed me too--that I hadn't been thinking very clearly. I need to think long and hard about fear and what it does to your head. There's a good lesson in there somewhere I'm sure. And I've learned that I'd better not tell the nuns about my reading. I'm sure they haven't read *The Three Musketeers*.

24

Remembering

WE'RE all standing in the side aisle in a straight line. All of us in the eighth grade class from Incarnation Grammar School are here at the funeral, wearing our uniforms. The Mass is over. It took place in our parish church and then everybody got into cars to come to the cemetery. But it's a part of the cemetery that I've never been in before. We're in a little chapel with marble walls full of the dead because they're not putting Robert in the ground but in a big drawer in a marble wall full of drawers. His coffin is sitting on a high metal scaffold, right in front of an empty drawer.

I know people who died before. Grandpa died quite a while ago. It was in the winter and everyone was afraid that they wouldn't be able to dig the grave because the ground was frozen, but they did. And Mrs. Campbell's son died in Normandy, in the Allied invasion. She didn't get his body back for months, but she changed her blue star to gold as soon as she got the news. Mother went to the funeral and kept saying that it was a great tragedy because he was her only son. And I guess he was pretty young too, just 24. But I've never known someone my own age who died.

Robert had leukemia and it all started with a nose bleed. Well, of course, it started before then, but there was no way to tell until he got a nose bleed that wouldn't quit. Then, when they discovered it was really leukemia, it was too late to do anything about it. He died six weeks later.

When he was in the hospital, Mrs. Wilson asked me to visit him. She said Robert wanted to see me. I really, really didn't want to go. Tootie thought it was because I was afraid of sick people, but I'm not. I've visited sick people before, even when they're in the hospital. It's not scary at all. It was because of the ring.

Last year, right in the middle of eighth grade, Robert came up to me and gave me the ring. It wasn't wrapped or in a box or anything. He just poked his fist out at me, opened it up and there was the ring, in his hand.

"I want you to be my girlfriend," he said. "Here. This is my grandmother's ring. This proves you're my girlfriend."

I almost laughed. I thought it was a joke. Robert and I had hardly ever had a real conversation. We talked about Civics a few times because he was mad about politics. But then I saw he meant it and I tried not to take it.

"No, here. Really. You have to take it. I want you to have it. I asked my mother and she said it was all right."

He was getting more and more insistent, his voice was getting louder and I was afraid people were going to notice.

"Okay, Robert." I took it. "Umm. Thank you, I guess."

It was sticky because his hands are always sweaty.

I didn't know what to do with it so I took it home and put it in the back of my underwear drawer. I didn't even tell Mother. I felt stupid and ashamed. I just put it in my drawer and tried to forget about it.

That's why I didn't want to go see Robert in the hospital. Mother encouraged me to go several times and even offered to go with me, as if she, like Tootie, thought I was afraid. I couldn't tell her why and so finally I went. It was just a week before he died.

I tried to talk about Civics, but Robert didn't have much energy for that. Finally he said, "I just wanted to see you. I want you to know how much I like you. I wish I could live long enough to have you for a girlfriend." I just couldn't say anything. I stood there, biting my lip like the ninny that was Dad's nickname for me. I wanted to blurt out, "Don't like me. Please don't like me. I'm not worth it." But I didn't say a word. Nobody would believe that if I told them. Sometimes I talk so much Dad says I must have been vaccinated with a victrola needle but just when I most wanted to say something, I couldn't. I squeezed his hand hard before I left.

Father and the altar boys come into the small room and Father asks us to sit down for a few words. I thought he said plenty at the Mass. He kept saying that the death of such a young person should make each of us ask if we were ready for death, which could come at any time. Instead I kept asking myself why I hadn't been nicer to Robert. I wondered if I was even ready to be a grown-up, much less ready for death.

But here in the mortuary room, Father talks more gently. He reminds us of the happy memories of Robert we will carry with us all our lives. If only, I think. If only my memory was a happy one. And then I start to cry.

25

The First Dance

I LOOK PRETTY GOOD. The green plaid blouse, sheer, with large bell-like sleeves suits me. It makes my eyes green and bright. The cut hides the fact that I have practically no breasts. The full circle skirt of blue-green taffeta rustles when I walk and suggests that there really are some hips under there. A little lipstick. There. Now a comb through my hair and I'm ready to go back to the dance.

I cross the gym floor through waves of noisy chatter and see Tootie waving at me.

"Come here for a moment and meet my date, Jimmy," she calls. "He's a sophomore at LaSalle." Tootie crosses her eyes for a split second. I guess Jimmy turned out to be a dud. Some friend of her older brother's.

"Hi, Jimmy. Nice to meet you. Are you guys having a good time? Hi, Marilyn."

Marilyn and her date are at the same table as Tootie and Jimmy. Marilyn is with Greg. They became friends just before we graduated from Incarnation Grammar School and Marilyn is practically glowing with excitement. At least she's not pawing all over him like some people. I look over at June as I think this.

"Oh, the band's about to start again," I say, "I've got to get back to our table."

"Who's the dark guy at your table?" Jimmy asks.

"Uh, he's Anita's date, her first cousin actually. Name's William." Guilliermo, actually, nicknamed Gilly, but he introduces himself as William so I do, too. "Gotta get back."

"He must be Italian," I hear Jimmy say as I turn away. "We have some of those at Cardinal Hayes."

As I sit down between Anita and Charlie, the band starts playing. "Blue Moon," my favorite song this week. I smile over at Charley. He takes my hand and we move toward the dance floor.

Charley and I dance comfortably together. We've been friends for years, all through grammar school. He's Irish and the oldest of seven kids; I'm the rare Catholic only child. He shares his family with me, and Mom and Dad offer our living room as a refuge where he can do homework in the quiet and watch "The Hit Parade" on our TV. He's even started to sing along with the three of us when we croon through the week's hits. We dance with ease and I give a small sigh of contentment. Then I glance over at Gilly dancing with Anita. He moves so smoothly. I really want to dance with him.

When the music ends we all troop back to the table and everyone is talking at once. This time Gilly sits beside me and he says, "So, you're good at Latin, I hear."

I look deep into his dark brown eyes and say, "I really like Latin. It's pretty . . . orderly, I guess. Well, not really. There're all those irregular verbs, I know. But somehow translating it is like solving a puzzle and I've always liked puzzles."

"She's good, Gilly. She's working on creating a Latin version of Scrabble."

"It's because I always lose at Monopoly. I need a game I can win."

Gilly laughs and the band starts playing "Blue Tango"—did everyone write a song about blue this year? Gilly whispers something to Anita, then he turns to me. "Dance?"

Charley takes Anita's hand, then we're all dancing again.

Gilly is as good as I thought he'd be. I feel his smooth rhythm and soon the music is flowing through my whole body. We swing outward, away from each other, then back together, this time closer than before. We dance on, Gilly leading me into steps and swings I've never done before. For seven or eight minutes we dance in perfect silence with a sense of oneness that makes me tingle. All too soon it's over. Back to the table, to comfortable conversation and the safe friendliness of Charley.

Anita Guzman and I visit the girls' bathroom together just before the end of the dance. We comb our hair and share our successes of the evening. Suddenly Anita catches my eyes in the mirror and turns serious.

"He won't call you, my friend."

"What?"

"I know what you're thinking. About Gilly, I mean. I saw your face when you came back from the dance floor. I even think he likes you. But he won't call."

"Why?"

"Because you're not Puerto Rican."

I stop to think for a moment. "But I've always not been Puerto Rican. And you and I have been friends for years." Well, for three years anyway, since Anita came to Incarnation Grammar School in the sixth grade. "We've eaten at each other's house and slept over even."

"Yes, but now it's a question of dating, not friendship. And being Puerto Rican or not matters."

"You mean that if Charley asked to take you to the next La Salle High School football game you wouldn't go?"

Anita pauses for a moment, then says, "That's right."

"But Charley is Irish and I'm Polish—half Polish, anyway—and nobody makes a big deal about that. Not anymore. Mother says it used to be forbidden: everybody yelled on both sides of the family when Aunt Justine and Uncle Tony got engaged. Because he was Italian. But that was in the old days; nobody cares anymore."

"Puerto Ricans care. Our parents do. It wouldn't be allowed. So Gilly won't call. I'm surprised he even danced with you. He says it's easier not to start something than to break it off later."

He says! Had Gilly asked Anita about me? Or better still, said that he liked me? Or could like me? But then, what was the point?

In the subway going home, Charley takes my hand and smiles, but we don't talk much. It's too noisy and, besides, I'm thinking about not being Puerto Rican. I remember when the signs went up in the shops on St. Nicholas Avenue, "Se habla espanol." I sounded the words out and wondered why I didn't understand them until Mother explained that they were in Spanish. But that seemed so long ago, seven or eight years at least. How could it stop mattering whether you were Polish or Irish or Italian and still matter that you were Puerto Rican? Maybe what mattered was who it mattered to.

26

The Duchess Wants Red Shoes

I SEE them in the March issue of *Seventeen*. At the bottom of the page are the words, "Sold at Macy's" so I go downtown to the 34th Street Store and look for them. I pick them up and they're soft in my hands. The leather is beautiful and I turn them over, admiring the stitching. They have a small white bow, nothing too much, and Cuban heels.

The salesman asks if I want to try them on and I say yes. I've worn stockings just in case. He finds my size and fits them carefully on and I walk up and down on the carpet, finding a mirror to see how they look from sideways. They look terrific. I breathe in deeply and begin to hope. I go back to the salesman, tell him I have to think about it and he takes the shoes and returns the box to the back room. I leave Macy's and go on to the main library where I'm supposed to be working on a report. The hard part is still to come.

Over dinner, I bring up the topic of shoes. Easter is not so far away and Mother and I are drawing designs for my Easter dress. Shoes seems a likely topic and, keeping the tremor from my voice, I tell her about the red ones.

"Red," she says, and her shock is all over her face. "That's the most impractical color in the world."

Practical is one of Mother's norms of reasonable behavior. Our shoes are always practical: saddle oxfords for school and one pair of dress shoes for winter--usually black--and one pair for summer--usually beige. When I graduated from Mary Janes--oh happy day--there was a long discussion about the most practical size of heel.

There's my dancing shoes of course, but they're in another category altogether. I remember going to order my first toe shoes, at Capezio's downtown. The attendant made me stand on a piece of tracing paper while he drew carefully around my foot. Toe shoes are made by hand to an exact fit. Now that I'm thinking about it, I think the red shoes remind me of those toe shoes. Something about the stitching, I think.

"Well," I say, "you could make me a red dress for Easter."

"I thought we had decided on lime green, with beige trimming. Then you could wear the beige shoes from last year."

"Exactly," I say, triumphant. "If we don't have to buy new Easter shoes, we can buy the red ones." I know there's a fault in logic somewhere in there, but I talk fast so that Mother doesn't notice. "You could make me a red dress for summer instead."

"But you've never worn red. I don't think you'd look good in red. You're too fair. The blue tones are your colors."

Before I can say anything more, Dad interrupts. He's clearly had enough of fashion talk and bickering.

"We can't buy you a pair of shoes that you'll hardly be able to wear. But if you want to spend your own hard-earned money on something so impractical, so be it. Maybe you'll learn the consequences of extravagance."

"That'll be the day," Mother mutters under her breath. But the conversation is clearly over.

I've gone hunting for every baby-sitting job I can get and together with my birthday money--Aunt Bertha never forgets, probably because she has a February birthday too--I've got just enough. So I'm on my way back to Macy's with the hope that they still have a pair of those red shoes, size 7 narrow.

27

Afterwards

AFTERWARDS, what I remember most clearly is that Tommy pointed right at me, just before it happened. That and my mother scrubbing the bottom of my uniform skirt and crying. But I relive that afternoon over and over again.

We're walking down the broad sidewalk from the subway stop on the top of the hill. The approach to the Bridge rises on our left and the tops of the bridge bump up against a brilliant blue October sky. "Miserable summer, miserable winter and October." Aunt Anna's mantra about New York weather echoes in my mind, but I don't completely agree with her. Some parts of winter are wonderful.

I love watching storms rage down the Hudson early in the season, whipping up the water like a gargantuan, invisible egg-beater. I always go walking during a snowstorm and feel like I should hold my breath in the silence the snow creates on the city streets. I never realized how noisy the neighborhood is until the snow shuts it into silence. But it's true that October has more beautiful days and nights than any other time of the year and a beautiful October day is exhilarating. We all catch the day's spirit.

We come down the street laughing, pushing into each other.

Tootie even skips a few steps, so lost in delight that she doesn't seem to care that she looks like a little kid again. We start conjugating Latin verbs in loud, sing-song voices. Then we put Latin endings on English verbs. "Snow, snas, snat." Roars of laughter. "Snamus, snatus, snant." It's such great fun. We're finally learning something new, something that wasn't taught in grammar school. Through it all, though, I keep track of Tommy out of the corner of my eye.

I've known Tommy Brady almost all my life. He was part of the fabric of the neighborhood and home, walking with us to school, acting as altar boy at church, carrying groceries for the older women. But I also thought of him as the bane of my existence, once I had learned that wonderful phrase. I discovered it in a Jack London novel called *White Fang*. I had lots of memories of his being bossy and even mean. Then, on my very first day of high school, Tommy spotted me on the subway and sat down beside me.

"So how's high school, Mite?" My size--I'm still the shortest girl in the class--had earned me the nickname and, much as I hated it, I couldn't shake it off.

"It's good, Tommy, lots of new stuff like Algebra and Latin. And Religion class is so different from Catechism."

"It's different, all right. You get to ask questions instead of memorizing answers. Boy, do I like that. The priests teach us, though, and you girls still have nun teachers, so maybe you don't get to ask so many questions." Tommy smiled a crooked smile. "Especially if your nuns are like Sister Henrietta."

Tommy and I had had the same eighth-grade teacher even though he was two years ahead of me. She stayed on and on at our school while the lively young nuns seemed to get transferred every year.

"Sister Henrietta once told me I had to go to Confession because I read *The Three Musketeers*." I rolled my eyes. "But the nuns we have now aren't like that at all."

After that first day, Tommy and I fell into an easy rhythm of going back and forth to school together. I go to Cathedral and he goes to Cardinal Hayes, but we both took the subway as far as 125th

Street before he had to transfer. We were always part of a larger group, but somehow Tommy always found a way to spend some time talking to me. I told him about Sister Carmelita who teaches Social Studies. She's so absent-minded that it's easy to make her believe she hasn't assigned any homework. We talked about Sister Theodore who's young and teaches Latin and makes it sound like the most exciting subject in the world. I even told him that I'm thinking of auditioning for the Girls' Chorus. Sister Theodore is the director.

When football practice started, Tommy no longer came home with us, except on Thursdays. The team had a strategy meeting during lunch on Thursdays and no practice after school. So Tommy and all the rest of the boys are with us on that Thursday and Tommy, his brother Jimmy and Billy O'Connor talk about football all the way down the hill. I remember how Billy invited me to play football with them that other October day in grammar school. Tommy hopes to make varsity and as we come to the last block before Haven Avenue, Tommy runs ahead of the others. "Going out for a pass," he shouts back.

That's when it happens.

A man in an old navy pea coat comes out of the apartment on our right and lumbers over to stand right in front of us.

"D'you kids go to Catholic school? Those are Catholic school uniforms, right?"

"Yes," we say. Then we freeze. The man takes a gun from his pocket and starts waving it around.

He starts to say all sorts of crazy things, most of which I don't understand. But I can't take my eyes off of the gun which is waving back and forth, up and down, right in front of my eyes. He shouts that all the Micks should go back to Ireland and that the Paddies in control of Tammany Hall deserve to be shot.

"Line 'em up against the building and shoot 'em dead. Like we did to those Eyetalians in Sicily."

He stops and looks at the gun in his hand, as if he can't remember what it is. We start to take a step forward, but he looks back at us and jerks the gun up so it's pointing at us again.

"They're all in league with the Pope," he screams, "And the Pope is an immoral bastard."

Tootie gasps and Marilyn giggles. Billy starts to say something, but the man steadies the gun in his direction and we all freeze again. Jimmy's standing right behind me and whispers in my ear, "Keep this guy's attention, if you can. But take a quick look at Tommy first."

I glance over the crazy man's shoulder. Tommy is slowly and quietly making his way back up the hill, with his finger on his lips telling us to be quiet. I look back at the man with the gun and try to hold his eyes on us. I hear Tommy's next step and I cough. Then I glance quickly at Tommy again and he points his finger right at me. At the same moment, the crazy man starts to turn toward Tommy who launches himself forward to tackle him.

The guy shoots Tommy in the head.

At the funeral, the priest calls Tommy a hero. When he tackles the man, the other boys are able to take him down and all the rest of us are safe. Afterwards, I try to remember all the other moments Tommy's been in my life--how he gave me ice off the ice wagon, how I kicked him in the shins over Rosalie, how he gave me the first ride on his bike when he got it. He was the first boy on Haven Avenue to get a two-wheeled bike. But afterwards, what I remember most is that he pointed his finger right at me before he tackled the guy. And I still don't understand why.

28

April Fool's Day

IT'S APRIL FOOLS' Day, after all. What do the nuns expect? And our tricks are all pretty silly and innocent, just a bit of fun. To be fair, Sister Anne Helene, in first-period religion, is a good sport about it. We all turn our desks around to face the back wall. When Sister comes in, she looks slowly and carefully over the whole room, then walks to the back, puts her books on Dorothy's desk and starts class. After a while, she goes into a really complicated explanation of some theories of moral behavior and says, "Sorry I can't write all these difficult names and terms on the board, Ladies. You're on your own for taking notes." Teachers vs. students: the score is tied.

When Sister Carmelita arrives for Social Studies, there's not a textbook in sight. We're all sitting with hands folded on the desks in front of us. Sister doesn't seem to notice. Tootie raises her hand and asks, "May I please go to my locker, Sister? I forgot my book." Then Anita raises her hand and when she leaves, June asks, then Mary Jane. Finally Sister says, "There seems to be an outbreak of the forgetfulness disease. Well, I'll have to improvise. Please take out clean notebook paper and pens. I want you to write 300 words on why we don't need books in class." Then she leaves.

I lay my head down on the desk for a moment, on the edge so I can peer over it and watch my shoes. I observe that there's a dark smudge on the white toe of my left saddle shoe and clearly visible because I've crossed my knees and my left foot is on top, swinging up and down. I start to count, trying to figure out if my foot is keeping some rhythm of its own. The big clock on the wall ticks audibly and, sure enough, my foot is exactly in time with its ticking. Oh, heck. This is getting me nowhere.

I take my pen and Pee-Chee folder with clean paper out of my book bag, then drag out my textbook and bang it down on the desk. Obviously we had never meant the trick to get all thirty-five of us to our lockers for books. I put my name on my paper, at the right-hand edge of the top line as always, then put my elbows on the desk and think. Three hundred words! That's two and a half to three pages, one side, no skipping of lines. The topic is almost as bad as "What I did on my summer vacation." Why didn't Sister just have us write "I must not play tricks in class" three hundred times. This is soooo boring. I loved Geography and History in Grammar School. Why did they become boring when they turned into Social Studies?

I look around the classroom. Tootie is writing feverishly. What can she possibly have to say on the topic? Mary Jane is twisting a lock of her hair around her finger and biting her lip. June has her mirror out of her bag and is checking her face. I want to tell her it looks just the same as it did yesterday. She carries that mirror around like some kind of lucky charm. Dorothy and Betty are whispering in the back of the room. Like Tootie, some of the other girls are actually writing, but without her feverish concentration. They're probably trying to compose an apology that sounds humble but with no groveling. Good luck to that.

I flip through my book, only vaguely hoping for an inspiration. The whole book is pretty boring when all is said and done. The pictures are all old and the pages are dirty on the edges, especially at the bottom and top corners where you touch them to turn the page. Since we rent our books from the school every year, there have been a lot of freshman fingers on these pages. I daydream for awhile about the girls who had this book before me. I wonder where they are now. Married with children, maybe grown children. Maybe dead.

I sigh and glance down at a chart that shows a comparison of industrial output for the United States between 1900, 1910 and 1925. 1925? Why did they stop there? I turn to the publication information. Published in 1930. This book is older than I am.

I think about all the changes in the world. Even the ones I can remember myself are pretty important. The changing European borders after the War and all those European countries going communist. We pray for the people there all the time. The independence of India--we read about Gandhi when we studied Civics in the eighth grade. Then there's the Atom bomb. That's changed everything. All of that only in my lifetime, short as it is, and Mother keeps saying that the changes since she was in school are almost unbelievable.

I think I have my essay topic. If our literature books are old--I'm gonna check this afternoon--it doesn't matter very much. Literature doesn't change. Shakespeare's "Merchant of Venice," which we're going to start reading in a few weeks, is the same as when he wrote it centuries ago. Of course, there's always new literature coming along, but everyone says you have to read the classics first. And you can get the new stuff from the library. But an out-of-date social studies book? I think I can just about get three hundred words out of that.

29

Thanksgiving

MOTHER and I are setting the table for Thanksgiving dinner. Dad's got the turkey roasting in the oven and the wonderful smell is beginning to compete with the pumpkin pie spices from earlier this morning. Mother polished all the silver carefully last night and now she's rubbing the crystal glasses with a soft cotton towel. After school yesterday I picked some leafy branches down in Riverside Park and they're in the middle of the dining room table, with some candles. The Aunts are coming to dinner.

Of course, the uncles and two cousins are coming too, but really we only think about the Aunts coming. My mother has six sisters and four of them live in New York, two here with us in Manhattan, one in Westchester County and Auntie Honey and Uncle Joe have just moved into a new house out on Long Island. She wanted to have Thanksgiving at her place but it's Mom's turn and these things are strictly observed. Besides, Dad's the better cook and his pies are legendary. There's pumpkin, mincemeat and apple, always apple no matter what the holiday, because apple is Dad's favorite. And there are always three, in case somebody doesn't like something.

There are six sisters but they won't all be here. Aunt Dee still lives with Grandma in Pennsylvania and Aunt Betty lives in Florida with her husband and my cousin Mike. But not even all four of the New York aunts will be here. That's because there's always at least one who isn't speaking to one of the others. Last year Aunt Justine didn't go to Christmas dinner at Aunt Honey's--her name's really Anna, but everyone calls her Honey--because she said that at Thanksgiving Uncle Frank had insulted her. No one else could remember any insults, but if there's an insult lurking in there some-where, Aunt Justine will find it. This year it's Aunt Bertha who's not speaking to Aunt Honey, which is hard to figure because Aunt Honey--she's my godmother--is nice to everyone. Nobody seems to know what the problem is, not even Aunt Honey. So there will be three aunts, three uncles, my cousins, Pete and little Billy. He's only five. It's gonna be a squeeze. We've moved the kitchen table into the living room for us kids and we can always talk Aunt Honey into sitting with us too.

Everyone seems to arrive all at once and Dad is busy pouring drinks. Most everybody wants a highball, but Uncle Bill, who used to own a tavern, asks for rock n' rye and gives Dad a bad time when he doesn't have it. Aunt Honey wants cream soda. That's what we three cousins are having. Dad teases Aunt Honey that she wants her hands steady for the competition. Two of the aunts notice great grandma's crystal candy dish in the living room and begin arguing about why Mother got it when great grandma died. "Why didn't it go to our Mom?" Aunt Genevieve asks and Aunt Honey answered that Mom was the oldest grandchild and great-grandma said she should have it. No one asks Mother.

After everyone's finished their first drink, Mother says that the food is ready. It's time for the competition to begin. Dad, the uncles and we kids sit down at the tables and Mom and the Aunts go into the kitchen. We can hear the shoving and the laughing and two of the Uncles roll their eyes. Those two managed to get a second drink and they're happily sipping. Aunt Genevieve comes out from the kitchen. She's shoved herself to the front of the line as usual. She's carrying five large dinner plates, three along her left arm and two on her right. She walks around to the head of the table, assumes a pose and then, just when you'd think she'd put the plates on the table, she goes back to the kitchen. Next it's Aunt Justine, then Aunt Honey, each of them carrying as many dinner plates as they can, without spilling anything.

When the aunts graduated from high school, each one came to New York to work. They had Aunts of their own to live with and they all got jobs as waitresses. Now, at each family dinner, they have to see whose waitressing skills have survived better than the others'. Aunt Honey can only manage four plates but Aunt Justine and Aunt Genevieve both carried five and Aunt Genevieve wants to have a playoff, but Uncle Bill starts banging his knife on the table and says that the game's over. The food's cold enough. So a tie is declared, the plates are delivered and we all start to eat.

The meal goes pretty well. Dad's stuffing gets applause and the turkey is done just right, juicy but with no bloody stuff dripping out. The cranberry sauce came out of the can perfectly, with all its ridges and grooves intact. The green bean casserole doesn't seem too good to me, but I hate green beans anyway so my opinion doesn't count. Billy picks all the marshmallows off the top of his sweet potatoes and leaves the potatoes behind. He's still something of a baby. When it's time for dessert, Dad asks everyone if they want apple, mince or pumpkin. Everyone chooses except Uncle Bill who simply says yes. He gets his usual slice of each, then heads to the big bedroom for a nap.

When dinner's finally over, everyone clears the table and Dad gets the cards and poker chips out. He drops Monopoly off at our table. I'm annoyed. I'd rather watch Dad play poker because I'm getting pretty good at it and trying to get better. But Mother says I have to be a good hostess to my cousins, so Monopoly it is. And it means I don't have to help clean up.

The poker table is pretty quiet. Uncle Bill is the only one who yells when he plays and sometimes he curses too, but he's still asleep. Uncle Tony hardly ever talks at all. Dad says that at their wedding, Uncle Tony promised to love, honor and never talk back, which is pretty odd for an Italian like Uncle Tony, but there it is. It's quiet enough so that we can hear the voices from the kitchen where Mother and the Aunts are cleaning up. For a long time, we hear laughter, then Aunt Justine's voice starts to get louder. She and Aunt Genevieve are arguing about something. We stop playing Monopoly and try to listen. But all we hear is the rise and fall of anger. Suddenly there's the sound of a dish breaking. Then silence.

In a few minutes, Aunt Justine comes out of the kitchen wiping her hands on a dish towel that she throws on the table, right over the poker pot. She pokes Uncle Tony on the shoulder and says, "Come on. We're leaving." She signals to Peter who gets up from the Monopoly game. I feel sorry for Peter. He's kind of red around the ears. I try to smile at him, but he's looking down at the floor. Billy starts to say something, but I kick him under the table. Dad gets up to get their coats and walk them to the door. I can hear crying in the kitchen and Aunt Honey's voice making soothing sounds.

When he gets back to the poker table, Dad and Uncle Frank divide the pot between them and then start to play gin rummy. Uncle Frank says, "I guess we won't be seeing Justine and Tony at Christmas." I fold up the Monopoly game and Billy and I play our own game of gin rummy. Billy was really too little to play Monopoly and mostly watched. But his dad has been teaching him gin rummy and he knows more than you'd think. Pretty soon the women come out of the kitchen. Mother's made a fresh pot of coffee and Dad gets out the brandy bottle. I give Billy a pile of my old comic books and settle down with my library book on the couch.

After everyone has gone home, Dad and I go up to the roof. It's really too cold for sitting, but we take our wool sweaters and one of Mom's crocheted afghans. We want to give Mom some time alone. She takes these Aunt events really hard. Dad and I joke about it, but Mom gets her feelings hurt and she's embarrassed by her sisters. Besides, it was her dish that got broken, the serving bowl from her good set.

Time on the roof is always time for Dad and me to talk seriously. Last summer, he started to bring up the subject of my future. He talks a lot about college. He and Mother weren't able to finish high school, but his favorite cousin Mary was the first in his family to go to college and he's really proud of her. She teaches Chemistry and Physics in the high school back in Pennsylvania and he's always telling me what a good life she has and how teaching is a great career for a woman.

I'm not so sure about college. There are so many things I want to do and I don't want to wait four more years to do them. Maybe I'll get good enough in my dancing to get into a show. I've watched the costume designers work downtown and I'd really like to do that too; I've actually started my portfolio of designs. I've even thought that maybe I'll become a nun. Nuns do things; they even run things, like schools and hospitals and orphanages. I can almost see myself running an orphanage, loving all those little kids that have no one else to love them. I tell Dad that college just seems to put being grown up farther away.

We sit quietly for a while. The stars seem brighter than usual and from up here you can't hear the street noise much. We watch the reflection of the bridge lights on the Hudson. Dad reaches over and takes my hand.

"You realize, don't you, Ninny, that you're gonna have lots of choices."

Dad hasn't called me Ninny in a long time, not since I was little. I look up and he's not smiling his usual smile. His eyes are staring at me hard. They're different from other people's eyes because one is blue and the other is hazel. Dad smiles so much that when he doesn't, it means something. I think about what he's just said.

"I know, Dad. I think about my choices a lot."

"You won't grow up to be one of the Aunts. The Aunts didn't go to college."

It's something to think about.

30

Chemistry Class

MARILYN and I are lab partners in chemistry, thank goodness. I don't think I could have gotten anybody else to go along with my idea.

In the beginning, I think chemistry will be fun and interesting. Finally something new to learn, not just more of the same old stuff. But wouldn't you know it, chemistry is full of math. Not just the same old stuff, but the same old stuff I'm not any good at. But I keep my hopes up and wait for lab sessions to start. That's something new and maybe math won't be so important when we're actually doing something.

When we start lab sessions, our teacher Miss Jenkins explains what she calls the micro-element method. We'll be using real chemicals and elements--in very small amounts of course--in the lab, doing experiments that allow us to observe and document chemical reactions and properties. It sounds exciting and I can't wait to start.

Well, it isn't very exciting after all. We have to put on large white lab aprons and they're backed by rubber and heavy to wear. And they slap against your legs when you walk. There's a peculiar smell in the lab. It's a little like vinegar, but it burns sometimes when you breathe in deeply. All of this seems promising. But for two weeks,

Marilyn and I follow the directions and measure out the small amounts of chemicals with care. Nothing ever seems to happen. Our lab manuals are virtually empty, except for the doodles I put in the margins during lectures. None of the other girls have much success either, although in one session, Tootie and Anita find something. But they can't identify it on their own. Miss Jenkins has to tell them what it is.

Finally Marilyn and I talk about it over cokes at the counter. She has her usual cherry coke and I have my usual lemon.

"There's just too little material," I say. "If something really does happen, it's too small a something for us to be able to see it. We need larger amounts."

"But there's nothing we can do about that."

I've thought about this a lot before I bring it up with Marilyn. "I think there is," I say. "Only one of goes up to get the stuff, right?"

Marilyn nods.

"So tomorrow you go up and measure out our chemicals and I'll talk to Miss Jenkins while you're doing it. Only you'll measure out twice the amounts. But we have to be careful to keep the same proportions." I know enough math to know that. We have to balance the equations, one of the few things I remember from Algebra.

Marilyn is all for it. And it works. We finally get a result we can put in our lab books. And we do the same thing for two more classes.

The other girls are beginning to notice that we're getting better results than they are, but Miss Jenkins doesn't seem to catch on. For a scientist, she's pretty unobservant. She just praises us for getting good results and gives us all a lecture on careful measuring. During the lecture, Marilyn and I keep our poker faces firm.

But after another week or two, the results don't seem all that great, so today we've decided to up the ante. We're going to measure out three times the amount indicated and it's my turn to do the measuring. Marilyn is great at distracting Miss Jenkins and I measure carefully, but I put in a little extra of one ingredient, just to be sure. It's only table salt after all; it can't possibly matter.

The results are overwhelming.

Marilyn and I watch in amazement as yellow-green gas begins to form. You can actually see it. Then Tootie gets dizzy and sits right down on the floor. Now everyone can smell it. Miss Jenkins hits the fire alarm and we evacuate the building.

We're out on the sidewalk now. Tootie's sitting on the curb and firemen are inside our school, wearing gas masks. Everyone keeps saying, "What happened?" and one of the firemen is questioning Miss Jenkins. I try to read her lips. She keeps shaking her head and I think she's saying, "I really don't understand."

It's November and cold out, but nobody stopped for coats or jackets. Most of us girls are bunched together for warmth, but I go over and sit next to Tootie and wrap my arms around her. Tootie looks up at me and I guess that she figures it was us, but she doesn't ask. I don't say anything. I just hug her closer.

I really don't think it was the little bit of extra table salt I put in at the end. I mean, really, table salt? But maybe it unbalanced the equation. We made a little too much chlorine gas.

31

Yet Another Aunt

I HAVE ANOTHER AUNT. I always thought that six was enough; when they're all together they take up all the space and air there is. You'd think there'd be some kind of family quota on aunts and that we had reached it, what with Mother's six sisters and Grandma's five. And then there's my Aunt Celia, really Dad's aunt, who is the kindest person in the whole world and the very best aunt I know. But now I discover there's another aunt on Dad's side of the family. I've never heard about her before and I may never meet her.

Dad doesn't talk about his family. I know he was an orphan. His father died, then his mother, then his stepfather. After that, he had to go to work in the mines and live with Aunt Celia. But he never talks about those days, just like he never talks about the War. When we studied American History, I asked him about what he did, what it was like. He put me off with some funny stories. That wasn't like him at all. He'll talk about anything with me, even sex, and why I don't always get along with Mother now. But not about the War and not about his family.

Well, tonight that changed. He sat me down after supper and told me about Aunt Katherine. She was his stepfather's daughter and I guess that he and Grandma weren't really married when she was born, just living together. Dad didn't come right out and say that, but it was pretty clear. Anyway Grandma's family didn't treat her very well, especially after Dad's stepfather died and they went to live with their Uncle Frederick. He kept telling her she was bad seed, had bad blood, and would go bad just like her mother. So she ran away. They never heard from her again.

Yesterday a letter came. Uncle Frederick's been dead for some time and Aunt Celia has been trying to find Katherine. She sent Dad an address in Harlem where Katherine was living with some Negro man. Dad took off early from work today and went to find her. It didn't turn out well.

Dad turns away from me and goes to the window. He rummages in his pockets for his cigarettes, takes one out and lights it. I can see that his hand is shaking. I don't say anything. The apartment is really quiet. The rain is coming down in sheets. I'm sure Dad can't possibly see outside the window. I can hear the sounds of pots and dishes in the kitchen, but Mother isn't singing as she usually does.

Without looking at me, he tells me that the other people in the apartment building said awful things about Katherine. When she finally opened the door to him, she cursed him with really bad language and told him to leave her alone. So he had to go away again.

Now I've seen my Dad cry a lot of times. He always cries at happy events, like weddings. In fact, I don't think he's ever sat through a whole wedding; he always leaves so no one will see him cry. But suddenly he's crying and it's a really different kind of crying, almost sobs. And he doesn't even mind that I see him.

32

Downtown With Friends

WE MEET by arrangement at the Subway Station at 182nd and Broadway. Tootie, Anita and I are on our way downtown to the Metropolitan Opera House. It's the first Saturday of May and it's absolutely gorgeous. There's a brisk wind from the Hudson, as usual, and even I agree that it's sweater weather, in spite of the brilliant sunlight. If it were my choice we'd go down by open-top bus, but we have a long morning ahead of us and need to be there early. The subway is faster.

The Girls' Chorus of the New York Archdiocese is holding its Spring Festival of Music at the Met this year. The Chorus is made up of all the individual glee clubs or choirs from the various Girls' High Schools and we only sing together once a year, at the festival. Each school sings two songs on their own and then, at the end, everybody sings the same last three songs. I've been in Chorus since my freshman year and the first two Festivals I sang in were in St. Patrick's Cathedral. But we couldn't get it this year and the Met was eager for good publicity. They're on yet another fund-raising kick for a new theater and gave the Archdiocese a good price.

When we get to the Met, girls are milling about everywhere and the nuns in black and white are like buoys in a sea of spring pastels.

We look for Sisters of Charity bonnets and Sister Theodore. She's pretty tall and we think she'll stick out. Or up, actually. And she does. The police have put up barricades keeping the traffic out of 39th St. and Sister Theodore is standing right on the corner holding a sign that says Cathedral High Girls' Chorus. We all gather there and wait until they open the Met doors and when they do, we move in ranks across the street. Sister Theodore has brought along Sister Anne Therese, with her clipboard and habitual glower, to keep us in line, literally and figuratively. At the door, someone from the opera company calls out school names and we enter in blocks, following our nuns.

I've never been in the Met before and I look around in amazement. Mother has gone to some of the Saturday matinees with her friend Helen Sartorus who has a job accompanying rehearsals, but I never wanted to go. It's enough to have to listen to the broadcasts with Milton Cross. Mother never misses one and the apartment has to be quiet while it's on. Dad says it's part of Mother's religion which annoys Mother who always mutters, "Don't be sacrilegious." But now I walk in from the lobby, look around and suck in my breath.

The balconies are faced with gold and each rises above the other. I count quickly; there are five levels of balcony. So the ceiling is way, way above us, ornamented with gold scrolls and paintings of 18th-century people in gold and red. It's bigger and more gorgeous than the Roxy. And it does feel a little bit like being in church. It's elegant, that's what it is, and I know exactly why Mother loves coming here.

But there's not a lot of time to stand around being impressed. We've work to do. Sister Anne Therese quickly gets us into the block of seats assigned to us, at stage right and Mr. Ross, the conductor, comes out on stage. Last year, he gave instructions from the pulpit at St. Pat's and made us all laugh with his remarks about elbowing Cardinal Spellman out of his job. Today he gets right to the point. We'll practice the three songs of the whole chorus first, then the individual schools will practice their separate pieces. Good news. Once we're done with our own music, we can leave.

There's a surge forward as everybody moves toward the stage, then the Sister Anne Thereses of the various Girls' Choruses gain control again and get us organized on the risers to rehearse the three common pieces. It takes a bit of time for Mr. Ross to get our voices to blend in "I Got Plenty of Nothing," our first piece, but after about half an hour we move on to a Stephen Foster medley arranged for three-part women's voices. That goes a little bit easier. But it's the last piece, the finale for the whole concert, that stretches us to the limits.

It's Mozart's *Jubilate Deo* and Sister Theodore was surprised that Mr. Ross chose such a difficult piece. I'm getting tired as we finish the Stephen Foster stuff, but as we start to work on the Mozart, my energy begins to come back. We've worked really hard on this piece back at Cathedral, but it begins to take on a completely new sound here at the Met, a place built for music. It's triumphant and exhilarating and eager, all at the same time. Mr. Ross is a stickler for perfection and he wants the loud parts really loud but mellow, and the soft parts, "hardly a whisper," he says, "but with a wide open mouth and full breath support." We spend a long time working on it and I'm glad to sit down after that and wait for our individual turn.

We have to wait through three individual group practices before it's our turn. I have a book with me and spend most of that time reading Gwen Bristow's *Jubilee Trail*. Then it's our turn and we mount the stage risers again to practice our two pieces, Palestrina's *Ave Verum Corpus* and a medley of songs from *Show Boat*. I remember that Ginger got a part in *Show Boat* when we went on that audition together years ago. I wonder what happened to her. The rehearsal goes well enough and soon we're done and off to lunch. Eleanor joins us.

We were going to go to Woolworth's or the Horn and Hardart but decide we've worked hard enough to treat ourselves. We check our purses for money and take a good look at our clothes. We dressed up for the rehearsal. We don't have gloves, but otherwise we're okay for Schrafft's, the one at 23rd Street and 5th. It's a bit of a walk, but we're up for it.

I love Schrafft's, we all do, and we get settled at our table with a lot of chatter. I watch the waitresses come and go--black dresses, white aprons and a smile on every face. I think about my aunts, waiting table in Manhattan as soon as they graduated from high school in Pennsylvania. I tell Tootie, Anita and Eleanor about the dinner party competitions, all the aunts seeing who could carry the most plates at one time.

"Only one of my aunts would probably have made it at Schrafft's," I say. "I can't imagine them smiling all the time the way the Schrafft's women do. Aunt Genevieve is too snooty to smile and Aunt Justine, too nasty."

Everyone laughs and so I tell a few more stories about the aunts, exaggerating their peculiarities just a bit. They're funnier when I tell about them than they really are when they're right there in the room. Then the waitress brings our menus and we settle down to choose.

"Look," Tootie says. "There's something called an 'Alligator Pear and Crab Salad.' It's the third item under the salads. What do you suppose an alligator pear is?"

None of us know, but we decide not to ask the waitress. We don't want her to think we're too dumb for Schrafft's! Tootie and I both choose the grilled cheddar cheese and pimento sandwich, with a coke. Eleanor can't make up her mind, but finally settles on a grilled deviled ham sandwich with iced tea. Anita says she always gets the same thing at Schrafft's: the special chopped chicken sandwich and a coke. The waitress smiles again, then takes our menus away.

While we're waiting for our sandwiches, I decide to tell everyone about my first ever visit to Schrafft's. I can hear Mother's voice in my head. "Don't monopolize the conversation, Annie." But I ignore it. Tootie likes it when I tell stories and I'm still all bubbly inside from singing the Jubilate Deo. I can't quite stop talking.

"I remember the first time I came to Schrafft's," I start. "I think I was about eight and I could read the menu pretty well by myself. When the waitress asked me what I wanted to drink, I said, 'a glass of burgundy wine, please.' Mother was mortified, but the waitress just laughed and brought me a coke. I thought coming to Schrafft's meant I was grown up and could order a grown-up drink, even though I was only allowed one tiny sip from my Father's glass at home." Everyone laughs and starts telling their own first visit to Schrafft's stories. "See," I say to Mother in my head. "It was a good story and got everyone talking."

Our sandwiches come and we start our lunch. We talk about school, our Easter outfits, and June's outrageous behavior at the last school dance, the one right before Lent started. When we're finished, Eleanor announces that she's going to Macy's. She has some birthday money that's burning a hole in her pocket. Tootie says she'll go too, just to see what they've got. They give us money for the check and leave. Anita and I smile at each other. We're going to linger. We don't get to Schrafft's very often and we don't want to rush it. The waitress brings us coffee. Schrafft's coffee is practically a legend.

"Anita," I say, "what's Gilly doing these days?" I haven't asked much about him since our freshman year dance, but I've wondered often.

"Oh, the whole family's worried about him," Anita answers.

"Why?"

"He's been spending every summer, or part of it at least, with his grandparents on the Island, Puerto Rico, you know. They want him to keep his Spanish up and he likes it because his grandparents really spoil him. Well, two years ago he was there for the Jayuya Uprising, part of the nationalist movement that is working for independence. Gilly got politicized and now all he talks about is Puerto Rican Independence."

"I haven't heard much about it," I say. "Wasn't there some kind of vote about it recently?"

"Yes, and the people of Puerto Rico largely supported commonwealth status rather than independence. Since the attempted assassination of President Truman, two years ago, most of the Puerto Ricans here in New York are against any talk of independence. They think that everyone will think they were for assassinating Truman. A couple of guys have gotten beat up for talking about independence. But Gilly won't stop. He tried to organize meetings at

La Salle at the time of the vote, but the Brothers stopped it. His parents are really afraid for him."

"Gosh. Why didn't you tell me?"

"What could you do?"

"Nothing, I guess. But I still want to know."

Anita just shrugs and we pay the check.

As we leave and head toward the Broadway local, I'm still thinking about Gilly. He's creating a story of his own, with no room for me, or even for Anita. It's one I'll have to watch from the outside.

33

Dancing and Dreams

I CAN'T SEE him anywhere. If he doesn't come tonight, I'll just die. He's the only reason I came at all. The band's already playing.

Mother and Dad enjoy these once-a-month socials at the Polish American Club. There's a potluck and Dad always brings one of his pies. He gets all kinds of compliments so, of course, he loves to do it. There's always a band, too, a funny sort of band, really, with accordions, some violins, some brass and usually a drummer. It's never the same musicians and not even the same collection of instruments, but they manage to sound reasonably like a polka band.

Mother and I love to dance and she usually divides her time between knitting and talking to other women, dancing (if she can find a partner) and keeping an eye on me. I can't remember *not* knowing how to polka; I think I could do it as soon as I could walk. At least I have a memory of being really small and having Aunt Anna put my two small feet on hers and lead me through the steps. If I can get Dad to dance with me, it's glorious and, when he doesn't, Mother and I get up and dance on the edge of the other dancers. We don't want to get in their way. But there are hardly any boys my age and the ones who come don't dance at all.

It was fun when we were all younger. Then all us kids danced on our own and chased each other around or sat near the band and watched. And there were always lots of desserts. But about a year ago, or maybe a little longer, the old men started to ask me to dance and since then it's been something of an agony. Mother says that I cannot refuse to dance if I am asked, not until I'm engaged or married and belong to my husband. I'm not keen on the idea of belonging to anyone, but I suppose I'll like it when the time comes. And I have to admit that the old men dance well, though sometimes they're wheezing by the end of the music. But some of them have long, bushy beards and when they swing me around, I somehow get scratched. And they smell of beer. I even stopped coming for a while, but a few weeks ago, Dad talked me into coming again and that night Danny appeared.

He came in wearing his naval uniform, so Dad immediately went over to welcome him and they got into a long conversation. Then Dad brought him over and introduced him to Mother and me. He's attached to the Brooklyn Navy Yard. His name is Danny Sorenson and, in spite of his last name, his mother is Polish and he's been raised with all the traditions, even more than me. Since that night, he's come to the social every month.

I see Mr. Sienkiewicz coming toward me from way across the hall but one of his friends stops him and I'm just about to bolt for refuge to the Ladies' Room when I see Danny come in the door. He's looking around the hall and I try to catch his eye and, when I do, I give him a big smile and he hurries over. He and Dad catch up on Navy gossip and then he asks Dad if he can dance with me. He always asks him. That's one of the things Mom likes so much about him. We move out onto the dance floor.

Dancing with Danny is nothing like dancing with the old men. He's got all the same polka steps, but he doesn't stomp like they do. He seems to be lighter on his feet, yet still firm and sure. His hand on my back moves me in the direction he's leading but he never pushes and if I shift my body ever so slightly in another direction, then he follows where I want to go. Somehow I always know when he wants to swing me out and back. There's something he does as a signal and I don't even know what it is, but I feel it and I'm ready for the swing. After a few polkas, the band takes a break and we go over to Mom and Dad. Danny gets me a coke from the bar.

Mother asks Danny about his family. She always does and by now she knows them all by name. They live in some small town in Ohio and they have to go over to the next town to go to a Polish church. She asks about his brother John, who is in his Junior year at high school--St. Ignatius High School where Danny graduated three years ago--and his sister Mary who attends the state college. Danny's grandmother has been sick all winter and Mother wants to know how she's doing. Dad interrupts with a question about the Dodgers. Dad and I are hard-core Yankee fans, but even we enjoyed the success of last year's Dodgers and Dad thinks the 1953 Dodgers will be just about as good. He loves Pee Wee Reese. Mother's always been a Dodgers' fan so she's been gloating since last October. Dad is trying to arrange for the four of us to go to a game and talks to Danny about getting us tickets. The Navy Yard is not all that far from Ebbets Field.

I get impatient and look around to see where the band members are. They're starting to walk back toward the dance floor, so I tell everyone to finish saying what they have to say because I'm ready to dance again. The music starts and Danny and I join the dancers.

After a couple of polkas, the band starts an *oberek*. That's a polka in double time and not many of the old men ever make it through an *oberek*. The dance floor thins quickly but Danny and I love this dance. It's made for stomping and Danny obliges, beating out the steps so quickly that his feet look like they're not even touching the floor. When the *oberek* ends, the band starts up another polka and Danny and I keep dancing. Then it's another *oberek* and we just move right into it. After that, even Danny and I are winded and we move toward the tables, looking for my parents. But Dad isn't around, probably in the kitchen, and Mother is talking earnestly with Mrs. Cominski in the corner. They're passing baby Robert back and forth between them, keeping him happy. So Danny and I slip out the door into the alley.

Danny leans against the building and I hoist myself onto the wall that hides the trash cans. Danny lights a cigarette, but doesn't offer me one; I don't tell him that I've snuck one of Dad's a couple of times and practiced looking like Bette Davis. We don't say anything for a while, then we start to talk about our favorite daydream.

"When I get married, Duchess," Danny says, and I love hearing him use my family nickname, "I'm going to have a traditional three-day wedding."

"Tell me about it, Danny," I say, "I've never been to one." So he does.

"The engaged couple go from house to house and invite all their family and friends personally. They only send invitations to those who live away and these are all personal notes, not printed things. Someone in the bride's family makes her dress. It's an honor and the best dressmaker in the family is chosen. Then for a week before the wedding, all the women in the family and lots of friends too start cooking: *pierogi, golumpki*, poppy seed roll, *chrusty*, even home-made *kielbasa*. Summer weddings are a problem, keeping the food fresh, I mean. One family I know even rented a big freezer and invited everyone to bring their food over and store it there."

"Gosh," I Say, "wouldn't it have been cheaper just to cater the wedding food?"

Danny laughs. "It's not about the money. It's just the way things are done. And you need a lot of food to keep everyone happy for three days."

"How does that work? I mean, where does everybody go for three days?"

"They usually hire the church hall for the first day with the band and huge tables set with all the food. Someone in the family offers their apartment for the wedding couple, fix it all up fancy and move out so the couple will have it to themselves. Sometime late in the afternoon, a crowd gathers to walk the couple to their wedding apartment." Danny looks over at me and reddens slightly. Then he continues, "Everyone else moves on."

"Where do they go?"

"Well, most of the time, someone has a large apartment to lend, but a lot of the guests are contented with a one-day wedding, so only the closest family--and some die-hard party-goers like me--end up going on. Record players replace the band, more food comes out and the party continues. People slip home or to a friend's house for naps when they need to. Sometimes the wedding couple returns for the second and third days, but not always. But I'm going to go to all three days of my wedding, I promise."

"Me, too. That's if I ever have a three-day wedding," I say. "They're not the usual thing around here."

Danny takes my hand, looks into my eyes and says, "Oh, Duchess, if only you were older."

I've thought long and hard about this. Five years isn't a really big difference, not if people are, say, in their twenties. But the difference between sixteen and twenty-one seems huge, even to Danny. Of course, I don't really think I want to marry Danny. We've only known each other for a few months and only here at the Social Hall. But still. When we're quiet together and sharing our dreams, well. . . . I lean a little closer to Danny and I'm just aching for him to kiss me. He would have, too, I'm sure, but just then the door opens and Dad sticks his head out.

"Hey, you two. They're putting the desserts out and if you don't come right in, you'll miss my apple pie. You know how fast it goes."

Danny drops my hand and lifts me off the wall. For just a second, he holds me close; then he turns and we follow Dad back into the hall. I let the door slam behind me and sigh.

34

Seeing Double

COURT CASES ARE BEGINNING to fascinate me. Here at the Main Branch of the Public Library, there are shelves and shelves of books on important legal cases and all their implications for the Constitution and the life of the people. Sister Mary Ignatius told us in American History that the Constitution doesn't mean much until the Supreme Court tells us what it means. That doesn't make a whole lot of sense to me, I mean, words mean what they mean, I'd have thought. But apparently not when it comes to the Constitution. I wonder if it applies to other writings as well. It's an interesting thought that sometimes authority might not have all the answers.

My topic is the court cases on the separation clauses. Sister said that when the authors drew up the Constitution, they had different ideas of what separation meant. Some thought it meant that the government should equally support all religions. Others thought that there should be no government support for any religion, which is, I guess, what we think it means today. But a lot of what those clauses came to mean was triggered by the Catholic schools. Stuff like whether the state could lend textbooks to Catholic schools or whether Catholic school kids could ride public school buses.

John Ireland, Bishop of Minneapolis, seems to have started the long debate way back in 1884 and there have been lots and lots of cases right up to our own day. In 1947, the Court decided that it was not against the Constitution for states to reimburse Catholic school parents for the cost incurred by their students' riding the public buses. It was a very divisive issue and there was a significant dissent written. So I've got lots and lots of material. It'll be hard to boil it down to the ten-page limit Sister Mary Ignatius set.

What really fascinates me, though, is how the lawyers argue the cases. It's all about logic and deductive reasoning. And a lot of it is about the meaning of words. I just love learning about the meaning of words.

And I love to argue. It's one of the things that most gets me into trouble. When I argue with Dad, Mother says I'm being disrespectful and tries to stop it. I know Dad likes it, though, and I think Mother doesn't like it mostly because she feels left out. But we stop arguing because Dad likes peace more than anything. Last Christmas I argued with Aunt Justine. Someone has to. She can be something of a bully, especially toward Mom. Later I heard her telling Mother in the kitchen that I was getting out of hand and I got the expected lecture after everybody left. Maybe I'm meant to be a lawyer so I can argue for a living. What a great idea. I've thought for a long time that I'd be a dancer, but maybe not.

Someone passes in front of the table and I look up just as a girl, a little younger than me, looks down. We both just stare. It's like looking in a mirror. Her hair is curly and mine is straight, but otherwise we could be sisters, no, twins. We stare and stare and then she turns away and goes to another table on the other side of the room.

Suddenly I think of that other aunt, Dad's sister Katherine, the one who lives in Harlem--at least she used to--and won't have anything to do with him. Does she have a daughter? If she does, does she look like me? We'd have only one grandparent in common and I've never even seen a picture of that grandmother, but still. I long to go over and talk to her, but something holds me back and I turn back to the court cases. When I look up again, she's gone.

People say that everyone has a doppelganger in the world. Is that girl my doppelganger? Or might she be my cousin?

35

Disbelief

"I THINK you're making all this up."

"I'm not. I swear."

"If you're right, why haven't we heard anything about this before?"

"I don't know. But I saw it with my own eyes."

Marilyn doesn't believe me and I can hardly blame her. I have a hard time believing it myself.

"What were you doing in a bus in Georgia anyway? I thought you were visiting your cousin in Texas?"

"My mother's cousin, actually. Cousin Agnes has been very sick and her family needed help. Well, we didn't have enough money to go on the train both ways so Dad got tickets home on Greyhound. Mother won't drive through mountains, even on a bus, so we had to go east first and then come north through Georgia. It was in Georgia I saw it."

"Tell me again." Marilyn sits down on the porch of the old mansion and pats the space next to her. Yesterday's rain had washed all the last dirty snow away and the late March sun had dried the porch and everything around. It smells like spring for the first time this year. Spring had already been farther advanced in Georgia when we rode through last week, at the end of Easter vacation. I sit down, close my eyes and start to relive that strange, frightening experience.

The bus pulls into the rest stop and I hurry to the door, even before the bus stops completely. I really have to go to the bathroom, fast. Inside the station, I look all around me. The bathrooms are usually at the back in those places and I start in that direction even before I really know where the restrooms are. Then I see a group of girls hurrying ahead of me and I just fall in behind them. We're almost at the back of the room when some lady grabs my arm and pulls me back. She really grabs me. I know I'll get a black and blue mark.

"Don't you see the sign?" she hisses, and points above the door. It says, 'Colored Only.' Then she swivels me around so I'm facing the other corner where there's another door, another sign. It reads, 'Whites Only' and she gives me a shove in that direction.

There's really no time to think about it, I have to pee too bad. But when I come out of the Ladies Room, I walk slowly through the station and look all around me.

The first thing I notice is that all the seating areas are marked by those same signs: Whites Only, Colored Only. I decide that I really didn't have a choice about the bathrooms, but I won't sit down in either place. Instead I walk over to where I can lean against the wall and keep looking. There's actually drinking fountains off-limits to one group or the other. But there's no sign over the candy counter. Right now there are no colored people buying, but I guess they could if they wanted. I walk over and buy myself some Good and Plenty and a Hershey bar with almonds for Mother.

The saleslady bends over to get a small paper bag for my stuff and then I see, behind her, another sign. It reads: We reserve the right to refuse service to anyone. That's really strange, I think. I can't imagine a New Yorker not wanting to make a sale. I go out the door to the bus parking area; I don't want Mother to worry that I'm taking too long. But I don't get on the bus right away. I need some fresh air and space after the crowded station so I walk past the bus to where there are dogwood trees, just coming into bloom.

I've never seen dogwood before. The flowers are lovely, four symmetrical petals that curl up at the ends and seem to hover above the branch like they were floating on air. I think some more about that candy counter sign. If I've never seen one in Washington Heights and it means that someone might willingly give up a sale, I think it has to be part of all that's strange about Georgia. It must be another, snooty-sounding way of saying to the Negroes, don't bother to try to buy something here. I get back on the bus.

"Did you talk to your Mother about it?" Marilyn asks and I jump and open my eyes. I've almost forgotten that I'm back home and telling Marilyn about it.

"As soon as I got back on the bus I went to my seat and waited for Mother to get back too. Then I gave her the Hershey bar and told her what happened. And that may be the strangest part of the whole business." I close my eyes again and go back into the memory.

"Hmmm," Mother says and takes a long time to unwrap the candy. I want to ask her something, but I'm not sure what the question is. Finally, the bus starts up again and Mother says, "That's the law in Georgia, Annie, and we're guests here after all."

"But is it right?"

"Is what right, Annie? Is it right to obey the law?"

"No. Or yes, maybe. But I think what I'm asking is, is the law right?"

"Wiser men than we make the laws, Annie."

"But that's no answer," I almost shout and Mother shushes me.

"It's like when I was little," I whisper. "You'd tell me to do something and when I asked why, you said, because I said so."

"Sometimes you ask too many questions."

That stuns me. Mother's the one who always tells me to ask questions. She says that's how I'll learn. But now? Why is this a question I can't ask?

"That doesn't sound like your Mother at all," Marilyn says.

Yes, I think. She always explains things, even things that I really don't care about. But I don't say anything.

We sit quietly for a while and I watch some other people squeeze under the fence and come down into the mansion yard. It's the only place where things grow wild on Haven Avenue and I look over at the lilacs growing in the corner nearest the river. I try to smell them, but we're too far away. I watch Sally, she of the scar on her leg, sitting outside the fence struggling with her new skate key. Mrs. Halloran is pushing her baby down the street in his perambulator. Her next one up, Willie, is pulling on her skirts and crying about something. It's a perfectly ordinary day in our corner of New York.

I notice Rosalie coming under the gate and wave her over.

"What're you guys talking about?" she asks when she gets close. Marilyn moves over and leaves space for Rosalie to sit between us. I don't say anything, but Marilyn gives her the short version of my story. Then there's another long silence.

When Rosalie finally says something, it's in a very soft voice. "This almost reminds me of the end of the war."

"Huh?" Marilyn and I say together.

"You remember the newsreels that showed the G.I.'s opening up the concentration camps?"

Marilyn and I nod. It took us months before we could get up the courage to talk to Rosalie about it and tell her how angry and sorry we felt.

"Well, I think what happened to the Jews in Germany started with something like this. Making them use different bathrooms, different stores, you know. That's what my Dad says. He says that's how it started."

We sit silent in the weak sunshine and try to let this sink in.

"It's worse than I thought," I say.

"Somebody has to do something." Rosalie's voice is firm. Then the silence closes in again.

"What can we do?" Marilyn asks. "It's happening in Georgia and we're in New York."

I think about New York, about the Negroes we see.

"I know that the Negroes all live in one section of New York," Marilyn says, "while we all live in another. Mother says it's because everyone likes to live among their own and the Negroes prefer it that way."

"I know. My Dad says the same thing. And sometimes I wish I didn't live among all these Irish. Present company excepted," I hasten to add, looking over at Marilyn. But she doesn't seem to hear the comment.

"But we all ride the subway together and sit next to each other. Sometimes. . . if it's really crowded." Marilyn adds the last bit hesitantly.

"There are public bathrooms in the subway," I put in. "Not that we'd use one. Ugh. But there's no 'whites only' signs there."

"Do you suppose the Negroes have to put up with things, even in New York, that we don't know about?" Rosalie asks. "I mean, we didn't know what was going on in Georgia?"

More silence.

"But I don't think that there's anything we can do." Marilyn says finally.

"We can pray," I put in. Marilyn just rolls her eyes, but Rosalie agrees.

"I'm going to talk to our rabbi," she says.

I think about Father Desmond. He wouldn't be any help, I decide. And I can't talk to Mother about this either. We're on our own. And we can't think of a single thing to do.

36

French Conversation

THE BABBLE of French conversation all around me makes my head spin. There's a French navy vessel in town and the captain is the cousin of Sister Aloysius, our principal. So she's agreed to let the first and second year French students come down to the French Consulate and meet with the sailors so they can practice their English conversation. We girls laugh hard at that. We're sure that's exactly what the French sailors have in mind. But we assure Sister that we welcome the chance to practice our French conversation also. So here we are.

At first, most of us are pretty much at sea--ha, ha. But the sailors look cute; they're wearing black beret-style hats with red pom-poms on top. And they seem hardly older than we are, so I get a little braver and start to mingle. I pronounce the phrases we're told they want to learn, things like, "the weather is fine today" and "where do you come from." The sailors repeat the English and we make them say it over till they get it right. Then they tell us the French phrase and make us practice in turn.

It's all great fun and there's a lot of laughter. I begin to hear the meaning in the flow of French around me. I guess my ear's getting tuned up. That's what Miss LaValle, our French teacher told us would happen.

I look up and notice Toni, one of the second year girls, going down a long line of sailors. Her name's really Antoinette and she has French grandparents so she thinks her ancestry means she'll learn the language quickly. She's got quite a big crowd of sailors around her, but she doesn't seem to be making much conversation. Instead she's created a kind of receiving line and is greeting each sailor in the line. She puts out her hand, which he kisses, if you please, then moves on. I go closer to hear what she's saying.

"Je suis charmante," she says with a smile. And each sailor replies, "Ah, oui, Mademoiselle, bien sûr." And then he laughs. The sailors in the line are poking each other, laughing and calling to their buddies who come over to get in line.

It takes a minute for the French part of my brain to get it. When I realize what she's saying, I grab Marilyn, who's walking by, and tell her what's happening.

"She's saying it wrong," I explain. "I'm sure she means to say, 'Je suis charmée,' I'm charmed. That's a very common phrase in meeting someone, but instead she's saying, 'I'm charming.' We need to tell her." And I start to move forward.

Marilyn grabs my arm, then she looks over at Toni. She shrugs and looks back at me. "Oh, I wouldn't bother," she says. "With her ancestry, I'm sure she'll learn the language quickly."

I pause for a moment. Then I turn back to the sailor next to me. "And where are you from?" I say, enunciating very carefully.

37

The First Poem

THERE IT IS, right on the page, in black and white. My poem. On page seven of the school's literary journal. My first poem published. The only junior to have something printed in the journal. I read the first line again.

"Autumn, not deceptive Spring, is love's true season."

Mother thinks it's about my feelings for Louis. Now Louis is a really nice guy. He's been hanging around since last summer and Mother likes him a lot. He treats me very, very nicely. When we go to the movies, he always walks on the curb side and takes my arm when we step off and on the curbs. He's Polish, too. That doesn't hurt, especially with Mother. He's got an after-school job at a printer's shop and in January he got tickets for an off-Broadway performance of "The Merry Widow." That night Dad extended my coming-home time so that we could go for hot chocolate and dessert after the operetta. It was a very nice night. Louis can be very funny sometimes. He's not so stiff after you get to know him.

He brought me violets for my birthday. They're very expensive in February. And he didn't even get mad when I said I wasn't going to movies for Lent. Anyway, Mother felt sorry for him and invited him to dinner a couple of times during Lent, so I saw him then anyway. He's a year ahead of me in school and getting ready to graduate. And he's got plans, good practical plans for next year. He looks at me very deliberately when he talks about his plans. His sister Gloria, who's in my class, has been going steady with Bernie who graduated last year. She says they'll be engaged as soon as she graduates. It's all a bit, well, too much.

But the poem isn't about him.

Last October a bunch of us went to see the LaSalle football game against Archbishop Molloy High School in Queens. It was one of those magical October days. The sun was warm, the wind just brisk enough to make you feel excited and the trees along Riverside Drive were aflame. Armand is the quarterback for La Salle and he threw a near-perfect game. LaSalle won, 24 to 14. Afterwards we went for hamburgers and Armand came in with several other players. He looked around, headed right for our table and squeezed in hard right next to me.

"I like your glasses," he said, looking down at me with laughing eyes.

I had gotten my glasses just the day before and I was mortified. Glasses! I was sure everybody would call me "four-eyes" or something. But then, at the football game, I realized for the first time that the players had names on their shirts. And I could read them. So maybe the glasses were okay, I thought. But then to get a compliment about them?

By the time we'd finished our hamburgers and cokes, Armand and I were all caught up in each other. He walked us to the subway and said, "I'll be looking for you, Annie."

We met a lot through the fall and right up to Christmas. Sometimes we just met at the luncheonette for cokes and then, when it got colder, for hot chocolate. On the weekends and holidays, Armand works for his father who owns a construction company out in Brooklyn. So it was mostly after school meetings. Once he tried to kiss me, right there in the luncheonette, right there in front of God and everybody! I pushed him away, but not very hard. I didn't get mad. You can't get mad at Armand; he makes everything seem like a joke and a compliment at the same time.

I haven't seen him very much since Christmas. I don't know why. He has a beautiful Italian name--Armand Guetchagrossa. It has a rhythm like music. I guess it's what made me write the poem. I read the last line again.

"We hug love close, against the coming cold."

38

Tootie's Great Expectations

I HEAR what Tootie's saying, but for a few moments I just don't take it in. She's crying hard but not wailing. Tootie gave up wailing about the fourth grade, but she could still win a sobbing contest if there was one around. Her sobs are loud and end in those gulping-in breaths like a little child's.

I put my arms around her, hold her tight, and say, "Stop crying, Tootie, and tell me about it. Where did this happen? And when?" No need to ask who. She and Johnny Halloran have been an item since the beginning of Junior year. I thought Mr. Antonelli had put a stop to it.

"It was in a cemetery, the Uptown Trinity Cemetery, last August."

Jeez, a cemetery, I think. But Tootie's going on. "It's a beautiful place really, full of lovely monuments and with lots of historic people buried there. They opened it when the Trinity Church cemetery on Wall Street got full up."

For the moment, Tootie's enthusiasm for the cemetery over-comes her anguish.

"We went there lots of times last summer, in the evenings when Johnny got off work. He loves history and we'd walk around and he'd tell me about the people buried there. The cemetery was the site of fierce battles in the Revolutionary War with George Washington leading the army. He knows a lot. Well, that night . . ."

Tootie stops talking and looks up at me. She looks like a pathetic little waif, I think. I've never noticed before, but she looks a little like Audrey Hepburn, with those large dark eyes. I don't say anything, so, after a moment or so, Tootie continues.

"That night he said he wanted to show me some literary monuments. He knows how much I love literature and want to be an English major. So he took me to the grave of Clement Clarke Moore who wrote *A Visit from St. Nicholas*. Then we walked over to another grave and it was the grave of Alfred Tennyson Dickens, the son of Charles Dickens. I was so excited. *Great Expectations* is my favorite novel."

The irony seems lost on Tootie, but I cringe. What she was expecting now would change all her other expectations, maybe forever, I think, but I don't say anything. I want Tootie to get on with the story. Tootie, however, is lost in the good part of the memories and, anyway, she can never tell a story in a straight line.

Finally she says, "There's a small cluster of trees near the Astor memorial and they form a kind of bower-like place. Johnny and I always go sit there when we're done with history. And," Tootie pauses for a moment, "anyway, we usually make out there, you know, kissing and, and stuff. We've always been able to stop before, you know, before things got too heavy. But that night, we just didn't."

I want to say just the right thing, so for a moment I don't say anything at all. Before I can figure out what to say, Tootie says, "It was just the one time, really, just the once. I didn't think you could get pregnant so fast."

Oh, Tootie, I think, where have we heard that before? In spite of all the horror stories everybody tells you, someone somewhere thinks it will be different for them. Now it's Tootie, my dear, dear friend, who's made the big mistake. It was time to get practical.

"What are you going to do, Tootie?"

"Oh, Annie, you can imagine what it was like to tell my parents."

I could. Mr. Antonelli has a fierce temper and he's very hard on Tootie. He stopped beating her years ago, and I'd already figured out that Tootie had taken up wailing because it stopped her father when he was beating her. Then he found lots of other ways to be mean. I like her mother. Mrs. Antonelli taught me to make pizza from scratch and now it's a frequent Friday night dinner at our house. I don't like fish. So I like Mrs. Antonelli, but she never stands up to Mr. Antonelli.

"Dad says I have to get married, right away. But Mother wants me to go to her sister's in Iowa, have the baby and put it up for adoption."

Iowa, I think, the last outpost of civilization. I wonder if Mrs. Antonelli has a relative in California, which would be lots better than Iowa.

"What do you want to do, Tootie?"

Tootie doesn't answer the question. She says, "Do you know what my Father did? He sent me to school to tell Sister Aloysius what I'd done. He said that Sister would make me truly ashamed of myself."

Suddenly I'm angry. That was just too mean. Tootie admires Sister Aloysius and likes her a lot. "Did she?" I ask. "Did Sister Aloysius make you ashamed of yourself."

"No." By now, tears are running down Tootie's cheeks, but she smiles, almost radiantly, and looks even more like Audrey Hepburn.

"It was a wonderful moment, Annie. She sat down with me in the auditorium and talked, really kindly. She said that she knew I was a good girl, with a lot of heart and generosity. That she knew I was ashamed of what I'd done, but that I should never be ashamed of myself or of my baby. The important thing was to make good decisions now and to be responsible. But she didn't tell me what to do. She said it had to be entirely my own choice."

Right, I think. Take that, Mr. Antonelli. Everybody seems to think nuns are as mean and narrow-minded as they are. I know a lot that are like Sr. Aloysius. I repeat my question. "So, what do you want to do, Tootie?"

"I don't know," she says and her face clouds over again. In fact, she comes pretty close to wailing. "Johnny says he wants to marry me, he wanted to all along, he says, and was just waiting till we were older. He says he's sure that the grocery store where he worked last summer will hire him full time and we can live with his parents till we save enough to get our own place. I love Johnny, I think I do. But I had my heart set on college. I love Johnny and now there won't be college and I'm not sure if I love Johnny enough." Now Tootie does wail, but just for a second.

Against a lot of people's expectations, especially her father's, Tootie had ended Junior Year with the third best grades in the class. Her essay on Washington Irving was chosen to be published in the school's literary magazine. Sister Aloysius, our principal, had told Tootie she stood a good chance of getting a scholarship and that she, Sister, would write strongly on her behalf. Tootie had spent all of last summer, well, all but the time she spent in the cemetery with Johnny I guess, collecting material on various colleges and their English programs. She had set her heart on Marymount College in Tarrytown.

My heart breaks for Tootie, but all I can say is, "Well, I guess you can't go to college, at least not next year, whatever you decide to do. You have to have a plan for now."

"If I do get married, I'd like you to be my maid of honor. I don't suppose your parents will let you."

I think back to Dad's mother and how she had to wait till his father died in a mine explosion before she married the man she was living with and how they had to get married in the sacristy and no one else was there except one of her sisters.

"They'll let me, Tootie," I say confidently. "You have to be sure about it though. Marriage is forever."

"I know. I think what I'm going to do is go visit my aunt in Iowa, just to take the time to figure everything out. I can't think at home. Dad starts growling and yelling every time he sees me and Mother yells back at him and then she cries. There's no room for thinking.

I'll probably come back and marry Johnny, but I'm just not sure yet."

"Okay. That's the first step and a good one. Time and space. That's what you need."

"Oh, Annie." Tootie's voice is soft and hurt. "What will all the girls say? They'll all know," she cries. "They'll know I've been stupid and bad."

"They'll understand, Tootie," I say, but I know they won't. They'll snigger and giggle and some will look pious and shake their heads. I know for sure that there's girls who have done just what Tootie's done and been lucky. They'll look the most pious of all. But a lot will ache for Tootie, like I do.

When I get home, I go straight to my room, stand by the window and look out. But I'm not paying attention to what's going on on Haven Avenue. Instead I'm thinking back to last summer and the night Marilyn and I went to the beach by ourselves. Marilyn's parents had rented a cottage in Jones Beach and one night after supper we went out for a walk, joining up with two other girls from our class at Cathedral. Then we ran into a bunch of the guys from LaSalle. One thing led to another, as they say, and soon we had coupled up and Larry and I found ourselves alone.

Now I liked Larry well enough. He was fun to be around, but we'd never really gotten to know each other. That night, however, we sat on the sand and talked a lot. There were whole sides of him I never knew. It turned out that he wanted to join the Merchant Marines, maybe right after high school. He knew all about the ships that used to sail from the Atlantic ports, how clippers were the fastest and how he wanted to sail in one someday. As I looked out at the water, bright with moonlight, I could almost see them. Then we started to make out.

Like I said, Larry didn't mean all that much to me. But when he started kissing me, it was if that didn't matter. It was like my body had a mind of its own and my mind was off somewhere on some imaginary clipper ship. I responded more than I really wanted to and started kissing Larry back. Then his hands began to move over parts of my body, the off-limits parts. Somewhere in my mind a tiny voice kept saying stop, this is wrong. But my body didn't hear. It was full of strange feelings, as if it was hungry somehow. We did stop in time, but only just. I was shaking all over and stood up, I wanted to run away, but Larry walked me back to the cottage and I sat on the back steps and waited for Marilyn. I'd calmed down by the time she got there and didn't say anything. Marilyn knew something was up, but she didn't ask. We just went in and went to bed.

I turn from the window and sit down on my bed. I have to tell Marilyn about Tootie, but I decide to wait until tomorrow. I'll tell Mom and Dad then too. I'm not sure how they'll react. They'll probably end up being sorry for Tootie and wanting to help. They won't be surprised that I want to defend Tootie all the way. But I don't want them to ask me about my own feelings. I don't want them to know how close I came.

39

Decisions, Decisions

IT'S a family celebration for Mother's birthday, August 16th. It's her 41st, which isn't a round number and Mother didn't expect a party, but Dad insists and Mother is pleased. It starts out well. Dad cooks a beautiful roast and there are roast potatoes and carrots to go with it. An apple pie, of course, in addition to a birthday cake for dessert. Mother has to bake the cake. She's terrific at cakes and Dad says if she wants a good one, she'd better bake it herself. So she does. It's an angel food cake with gooey chocolate frosting. Everything is going along beautifully when the question of college comes up.

Dad has mentioned college off and on over the years and from the beginning of junior year he brought it up whenever he could get it into the conversation. He practically adores his cousin Mary who was the first person in the family to go to college and he sings her praises long and hard. Then just before Christmas of junior year, Sister Mary Eleanor, my home room teacher, called my parents in and the three of us sat in the faculty lounge. She talked about my grades and test scores, described local colleges, public and Catholic, and the possibilities of scholarships. Well, after that, it seemed like there was no going back, not for Mother and Dad at least.

Today Aunt Justine starts it, as usual. We're all in the living room by now, eating the second dessert, whatever we didn't have the first time around, and more coffee. I'm on the apple pie.

"So, what's all this fuss about college?" she asks, sweeping her eyes from Mom to Dad to me. My mouth is full of apple pie and I can't answer, so Dad responds.

"It's not a fuss, Justine. We're just talking about Annie's future. The nuns think she should go to college. She has all the scores and grades that will get her in." Dad can't keep the pride from his voice and he gives me a big smile.

"Yes, well. No one's surprised by that. That girl always has her nose in a book. You're too soft on her, Teresa. She should have had a part time job before this. She needs to find out how hard it is to get on in the world. She should already be contributing something to the family like we had to. Who listens to nuns anyway? What do they know about life?"

Aunt Anna speaks up. "We needed to go to work. Annie doesn't. She should be free to do what she wants. College is getting to be important."

"What do you know about it? You refused to go to high school. You were the first of us who could have gone. But you quit. I would have given my eye teeth to go and you just walked away from it. Besides that was high school. College isn't important for girls."

Leave it to Aunt Justine to say something hurtful to Aunt Anna, I think. But for once, my godmother doesn't back down.

"If you would have given your eye teeth to go to high school, you should understand Annie's desire to go to college. Why do you always have to be against things?"

Before Aunt Justine can go down that road, Dad jumps in. "What do you mean, college isn't important for girls? My cousin, Mary, . . ."

Mother interrupts then. "They all know about Mary, Edward." She looks hard at me. It's my turn.

"I'm going to college," I say and I'm surprised at how sure my voice sounds. "That's already been decided. The only real question is where." It hadn't really been decided. Mother and Dad have left it to me and, though I keep thinking that I'm not sure, suddenly I am and I say it out loud for the first time. Maybe it was hearing Aunt Justine say it wasn't important for girls. I suddenly realize that it is important for me.

There's a long silence and everyone is looking at me. I sigh. I guess they get the whole story.

"There's Misericordia College back in Pennsylvania." And I don't get any farther. All the Aunts start talking at once, even Aunt Genevieve who hasn't said a word up to now.

"A Catholic college?" Aunt Justine sounds disgusted.

"Oh, good," says Aunt Anna, "There's lots of family there. You could live with one of them, or at least visit."

"Isn't City College good enough for you?" Aunt Genevieve asks. "We certainly pay big bucks in taxes. Someone in the family should get something out of it."

"She's had enough Catholic training, Teresa." Aunt Justine turns on Mother. "If you're not careful, she'll end up just like you, always running off to church on one excuse or another."

"Now wait a minute, Justine." Dad starts to object, but I cut him off and make a big mistake.

"You could do with a little more church yourself, Aunt Justine."

The silence is profound. I see Mother close her eyes and one tear squeezes through. I know well that Aunt Justine will take that remark out on Mom. Besides, my snottiness hurts her more than her sister's meanness. When will I ever learn?

Aunt Anna tries to rescue me. "Where are your friends going, Anushka? I suppose some of them are going too?"

"Marilyn's going to CUNY. She told Mom that City College was on Convent Avenue so it was practically Catholic. Our friend Tootie isn't going."

"Isn't she the one that's getting married any day now? Are you in the wedding?"

"Yes, she is, Aunt. The wedding is in two weeks and I'm the maid of honor. It's a small wedding."

"That's nice," Aunt Anna croons, "better to save the money for their apartment, rather than spend it on a big wedding."

They're saving the money for the baby, I tell Aunt Anna in my head, and it's not nice at all. We tried not to talk college in front of Tootie, but I can't forget the sorrow I saw in her when she realized she couldn't go. Tootie wants to go to college, almost more than the rest of us.

"I think it's down to City College or Misericordia," I say. That's not quite the whole truth, but I don't want to say any more. Why do the Aunts have to pick over everyone's life as if it were leftover turkey?

But Aunt Justine isn't finished having her say.

"I hope you don't think you can borrow from us to pay for Misericordia." She looks over at Uncle Peter who, as usual, says nothing.

Aunt Anna looks over at Uncle Frank, who's sitting there looking out the window as if nothing of this interests him. But then he shakes his head and Aunt Anna stammers, "We'd like to help. I'm her godmother, after all, and she's named for me, but . . . "

Aunt Justine interrupts her.

"Well, Miss High and Mighty, I've got an idea. If you're determined to go to an expensive college, I know just how you can pay for it. Get a job as a live-in maid. Those relatives that Anna keeps on about can help you find a good place. Most of us started out cleaning houses when we were a lot younger than you are. It's honest work and it's time you learned to stand on your own two feet."

Mother looks thoughtful, as if she's actually considering the possibility, but Dad puts his foot down. "It's no time to be going backwards," he said. "This family is moving forward."

He stands up. The conversation is at an end.

"Who wants more coffee?" he asks. "Another piece of apple pie, Bill? Or do you want more of Teresa's angel food cake? Anyone for brandy?"

Everyone takes Dad's hint and starts to talk about something else. Dad and Uncle Bill start to argue about the merger between the AFL and CIO that George Meany is working for.

"John L. Lewis is against it," Dad says, "and I've always got to go along with the United Mine Workers."

"You've been out of the mines for years," Uncle Bill protests.

"Yeah, but still," Dad says. "I'm still a working man and the union is the only protection a working man has. The bigger, the better, I say."

And they're off. Uncle Bill doesn't actually know how to talk in a normal conversational tone and when he and Dad argue, no one else can hear himself think. When Uncle Bill starts with the "god-damns," the aunts move into the kitchen and I go to my room. I'm embroidering pillowcases for Tootie's wedding gift and still have lots to do. Nobody stays late and soon we've all said good-bye at the front door. I wait for the ax to fall.

Mother doesn't even mention my nasty remark to Aunt Justine. All she says is, "Why didn't you tell them the rest of it?"

I want to tell her it's none of their business, but I don't want to hurt her any more than I've already done.

"It was just too complicated. They all want me to fall into line somehow and I'm not ready yet."

Back in January, I did think that if I went to college--a big if--it would be either City College or Misericordia. Then Sister Helen Marie threw everything up for grabs again.

Sister Helen Marie taught me in the second grade and she and Mom have remained friends ever since. Her community has a college in San Diego, California, and she went to work on my behalf. In April, right after Easter--Mother said that was a sign--we got a letter from the college. They offered me a scholarship that covered all the tuition for four years, on condition that I keep up my grades. Well, the discussion began all over again.

Mother, of course, was against my going so far from home. Dad was all for it. He's wanted to go to California ever since he was stationed there during the war, but Mother doesn't want to move so far from her family. When the letter came, Dad was jubilant.

"If you go to Mount Seton College, we'll have a reason to visit." He winked at me. He's still hoping he can convince Mother to move. Once she sees California.

The problem is the cost of boarding at the college. Sister Helen Marie said that once I was there, I could get one of the on-campus jobs, maybe even as a resident advisor in the dorms, which gives you room and board. The problem, of course, is that I'd have to pay residence fees for the first year, at least. That makes Mount Seton a lot more expensive, to say nothing of the train fare.

"Besides, Mount Seton and California is just a dream, Mom," I say, "the aunts already think I'm nothing but a dreamer. They don't have to know about the California dream."

Mother doesn't say anything more, but goes around the living room, turning off the lights and gathering up cups and glasses.

"Keep dreaming, Ninny," Dad uses my baby name as he gives me a hug. "Dreams sometimes come true. Look at me, I married your mother. But now it's time for sleeper's dreams." We all go off to bed.

40

Going Away

I SIT BACK in the seat and buckle the seat belt. My purse is on the floor in front of me and it's new for this trip, big enough to hold my book, my travel documents and a couple of candy bars. I breathe deeply and look out the window. They're still loading the baggage and I stare at the rolling cart to see if I can find mine. I can't see it. It must be already in the dark belly of the plane. I hope.

Dad's given me all the statistics on how safe flying is, but as the plane starts to move I get nervous anyway. I say an "Act of Contrition," just in case, and try not to hold onto the armrests too hard. I don't want the old lady in the seat next to me to think I'm scared. She's just opened up her knitting and is calmly working away. I listen carefully to the instructions about safety. I can't imagine needing life vests or flotation devices anywhere across the U.S. but I'm glad there will be oxygen available.

I watch out the window as the plane takes off from La Guardia. As it climbs, I keep my eyes fixed on the Hudson, pick out the George Washington Bridge and look hard for our street. Good-bye, Haven Avenue. I'm off to California.

The stewardess comes down the aisle handing out earphones. There's a magazine in the pocket on the seat back in front of me that tells about the stations with different kinds of music. Before I can figure out how to work everything, the lady next to me has herself plugged in and she sits back with her eyes closed and a smile on her face. I find the jazz station and sit back to listen to Benny Goodman play "Fascinating Rhythm." I remember the dance steps we did in tap class and my feet move around a bit.

Then the stewardess comes along again and asks each of us what we'd like to drink. The knitter next to me asks for tea and I ask for a coke. Since the knitter has unhooked herself and looked up, I turn to her and say, "I'm Anne and I'm going away to college."

I've practiced this statement by myself, saying it to the mirror, but this is the first time I've said it out loud to someone else.

"That's nice, dear," she says.

Nice, I think. Nice? It's wonderful. And I'm scared to death. But I only ask her if she's going home or going on a trip.

"I'm going home, dear. I've just been visiting my grandchildren." Then she puts the earphones in again, takes her pattern book out of her purse and continues her knitting. I listen to Goodman play "Where or When," and that starts me thinking. Where or when, but mostly how, did it all turn out that I'm on this plane? When I finally decided that I really did want to go to college, it became seriously a matter of money. City College was cheap enough, but the two Catholic colleges, especially Mount Seton College in San Diego, cost quite a bit more money than we had.

The stewardesses are coming around again, this time with our meals. We get served lunch on this flight. I choose the steak and when I unwrap everything I find that it comes with a salad and creamy potatoes of some kind. There's a square of chocolate cake too and I choose another coke to go with it. It's all pretty good, but the steak is overdone. I'm the daughter of a butcher and we all prefer our beef rare. But I enjoy it anyway. My seat companion leaves her earphones in so there's no chance at lunch conversation. It's just as well. I still have a lot to think about, to remember.

Like how I tried to sell my "just-in-case" pin, the one Aunt Anna gave me for my seventh birthday. I thought that college was really like the "just-in-case" situations that Aunt Anna talked about so long ago, when she gave me the pin and I overheard her and Mom talking about it. Jewelry was just in case a woman needed to get away and I thought that college qualified, so I took it to a jeweler's up on Broadway. But he said it was only worth about a hundred dollars. A lot of money, I thought, but not enough.

I remember the day Dad came home and called Mother and me into the living room.

"We've talked about this college thing long enough," he says. "It's time for a little action. I've cashed in some of our war bonds and put the money in a savings account. It's enough to pay for one semester living on campus at Mount Seton College. You'll have that much time, Annie, to find an on-campus job or even a waitress job off-campus. But there's one condition," he said, looking at me hard. "You're not to work as a maid."

"Edward, that's our retirement money," Mother protested

Dad smiled and said, "We'll make the duchess take care of us in retirement. The ball's in your court, Kiddo. Now it's not about money, it's about what you really want to do."

So here I am. "I'm Anne and I'm going to college," I mutter to myself.

Suddenly it seems as if the bottom drops out of the world. The plane bounces or something. It rights itself for a minute, then drops and bounces again. The "fasten seatbelt" sign comes on with a ping and my seat companion actually drops her knitting in her lap and grabs both of the arm rests. I wonder briefly if the act of contrition I prayed during take-off is still in effect. And I look up over my head to see if that oxygen thing is coming down; I'm finding it hard to breathe. Then comes the calm voice of the Captain: "We've come upon a bit of weather, folks. There's nothing for you to worry about, but we've put the seatbelt sign on and ask you to keep your seats. We're trying to climb above the storm and should be clear in ten or fifteen minutes."

I take a few more deep breaths and go back to remembering.

Yesterday was hard. All I wanted to do was visit friends and say goodbye to Haven Avenue. I wanted to climb up on the bridge again and look down on Henry Hudson's river. I wanted to visit the corner store where, during the war, Mr. O'Halloran gave us a glass of soda water for two cents when we didn't have a nickel for a coke. I wanted to sneak into the grounds of the old house on the corner, the one we called the mansion. It's been sold finally to a developer who's going to build some new apartment buildings. So it won't be here when I come home. Haven Avenue will be different. The bridge will be the same, I guess, but I bet when I stand on it and squint down into the water, Henry Hudson's ship won't sail before my eyes anymore. And I wanted to do all these things alone. Anyway Tootie has moved with Johnny and their baby to Chicago where Johnny's gotten a better job, and Marilyn had a date with Joe. She said she'd break it, but I told her not to bother. I really wanted to be alone.

But Dad can't imagine missing an opportunity for a family dinner. So all the aunts were invited, with the uncles and cousins of course. He baked a ham, made scalloped potatoes and coleslaw and, of course, three kinds of pie. Uncle Bill did his usual one slice of each, then went for a nap. But everyone else sat around forever and talked about my future and their pasts. The latter were obviously more interesting to them and I was pretty much out of the conversation. But Aunt Justine took me aside before she left and gave me a ring. It's very fancy and I don't like it much, but I guess now I have two pieces of "just-in-case" jewelry. I was going to leave them at home, but I decided there might be a "just-in-case" situation ahead of me in California, so I sewed them into the lining of my suitcase. It's safely in the hold. I hope. It will greet me in California.

Again, the stewardesses interrupt my train of thought as they come down the aisle, picking up the lunch things. It's a good interruption. It's time to start thinking about California, enough of this looking back, as Dad says.

The college sent me a letter two weeks ago, so I know a little bit about what's coming. A senior girl will be meeting me at the airport, one who has her own car, the letter said. Wow. I'm wearing my new suit and I look down to see how wrinkled it's getting. There's nothing I can do about it, so I think about how to talk to a senior girl with her own car.

Clothes have kept Mother and me busy all this summer. We pored over *Seventeen* and the Butterick pattern books, piecing together what we hope is an adequate college wardrobe. I've worn uniforms all my life, so I've never had to think about school clothes before. At Cathedral we wore navy serge jumpers as ugly as sin and right before school started every September, the nuns held a trading fair in the auditorium. If you brought your old uniform in bearing a cleaner's tag, you could exchange the one you'd outgrown for a larger size. The only one I ever bought was the first. I don't know what those God-awful things were made of; they never wore out, just got shinier and uglier as they passed from hand to hand. At the last minute, I tucked my red shoes into the suitcase. They don't go with anything else in there, but I still love those red shoes.

All the freshmen are arriving today. Tomorrow and on Monday, Labor Day, there will be activities, "designed to orient new students to the life and culture of Mount Seton Catholic Women's College." I quote the letter in my head and try to imagine all the activities, besides classes, that make up the life and culture of the place. I suppose Cathedral High had a culture, though I never thought about it and no one ever called it that. Whatever I imagine about the world ahead of me, it will be completely different from the places I know best: Haven Avenue, Incarnation Parish, the Bridge, the Loew's up on St. Nicholas Avenue. It's going to be so wonderfully different. After all, it's California. So why am I starting to feel homesick? I wonder if any of the girls in the dorm like to play poker.

I've been assigned a roommate. Her name's Maria Rodriguez so I guess she's Puerto Rican. I wonder if she has a handsome cousin who dances like Gilly. Maybe in California they won't care that I'm not Puerto Rican. I've never had to share a room before. I hope Maria and I get along. What happens if your roommate turns out to be a pain in the neck? Do they let you change? I think back to Joanie and the swimming pool, how she said I thought I knew everything and always had my hand up. I wonder if college girls are like Joanie and if I'll have to keep pretending that I don't know things. I probably don't dare. I have to keep my grades up or the scholarship goes away and it won't be as easy as it was at Cathedral.

I look over at my companion. Her knitting has fallen in her lap and her head is lolling back in a doze. There's a dribble coming out of her mouth and I want to reach over and wipe it away, but of course I don't. I can't possibly sleep myself, so I take my book out of my bag, tilt the chair back a little and put on the overhead light. It's Dumas' *The Count of Monte Christo.* I know it's on the Index of Forbidden Books, but I've given myself permission to read it. I'm going to be an English Major and a French minor--I've read all about the requirements in the catalog--and I have a lot to learn.

My name is Anne and I'm going to college.

Made in the
USA
Middletown, DE